COMPOSITE CONSTRUCTION
IN STEEL AND CONCRETE

COMPOSITE CONSTRUCTION
IN STEEL AND CONCRETE
FOR BRIDGES AND BUILDINGS

IVAN M. VIEST

Bridge Research Engineer, AASHO Road Test

R. S. FOUNTAIN

Bridge Engineer, Portland Cement Association

R. C. SINGLETON

*Vice-President of Engineering, Nelson Stud Welding
Division of Gregory Industries, Inc.*

McGRAW-HILL BOOK COMPANY, INC.

New York   Toronto   London

1958

Composite Construction in Steel and Concrete

Library of Congress Catalog Card Number: 58-7428

THE MAPLE PRESS COMPANY, YORK, PA.

PREFACE

Composite construction is an improvement of the commonly used concrete slab–steel-beam type of construction. Instead of merely resting on the steel framing, the slab in composite construction is made to aid the steel beams in carrying the loads.

Since coming to the fore about 1935, composite construction has established its place firmly in the bridge and building fields. In particular, composite highway bridges gained general acceptance, and their design became fairly uniform through early publication of specifications, which presented basic design principles.

Nevertheless, the aids now available to designers are relatively few, and most of them are not in a form suitable for ready reference. This book was prepared as a design aid to fill the gap. Because composite bridges are more common than composite construction for buildings, more emphasis is placed in the book on bridge design.

The text follows the latest highway bridge specifications of the American Association of State Highway Officials (AAHSO) and embodies the results of several recent investigations. It presents design formulas and tables and graphs for preliminary designs. For the designer not experienced in composite design, it contains also explanations of the basic principles and several design examples. However, the reader is assumed to be familiar with ordinary design of concrete slabs and steel beams.

The reader who wishes to study composite construction in more detail and to get acquainted with the background of the material presented in this book can refer to the publications listed in the last chapter for more information.

The major problem in the design of a composite beam is the selection of its cross section. In general, a large number of combinations of concrete-slab thickness and steel beams is possible.

Thus, the selection of slab and beam dimensions requires a trial procedure.

Two simple design methods are presented—one limited to beams with rolled steel sections and the other applicable not only to these beams but also to rolled steel sections with cover plates and to built-up plate girders. The first method is based on tables giving properties of composite sections, and the second on simplified equations, which can be solved by simple graphs in the book.

The methods for selecting the cross section of a composite beam are given in Chap. 2. It includes also equations for computation of stresses after the cross section has been selected, formulas for computing length of tension cover plates, and discussions of composite design for continuous beams and of deflection computations.

Whether or not the partnership of concrete slab and steel beams is successful depends on the means used to make them work together. Usually, shear connectors are attached to the top flange of the beams for this purpose. Design of shear connectors is dealt with in Chap. 3.

Formulas given for the capacity of stud, channel, and spiral shear connectors and for the safety factor are the same as those required by the latest AASHO specifications. Comparisons of the three types of connectors and data on the properties and use of stud connectors also are included in Chap. 3.

Manuscripts of individual chapters were submitted for comments to several well-known designers experienced in composite construction, and their suggestions were valuable in improving the book. The authors wish particularly to acknowledge their indebtedness to Charles H. Clarahan, whose encouragement and helpful criticism contributed substantially to the completion of the book. Suggestions and comments received from E. F. Gifford, Simon Miller, Philip P. Page, Jr., L. Nordlow Rian, Kenneth R. Scurr, and C. A. Sutermeister were of invaluable help, and the authors wish to express their gratitude for the generous advice. Thanks are also extended to Frederick S. Merritt, Senior Editor, *Engineering News-Record*, for editing the manuscript.

The studies and work resulting in this book were planned and coordinated by I. M. Viest, bridge research engineer, AASHO

Road Test (formerly research associate professor at the University of Illinois), at the request of Nelson Stud Welding Division, Gregory Industries, Inc. The design methods and examples were prepared by R. S. Fountain, bridge engineer, Portland Cement Association (formerly senior bridge designer of the Georgia State Highway Department), and the sections on granular-flux-filled shear-connector studs were prepared by R. C. Singleton, vice-president of engineering, Nelson Stud Welding.

Ivan M. Viest
R. S. Fountain
R. C. Singleton

CONTENTS

NOTATION

a = distance of the maximum-moment section from mid-span (Fig. 2-8) or distance shown in Fig. 2-9

A = numerical factor depending on the properties of the composite beam and on the design requirements, usually taken as 2.7

A_b = area of bottom flange of plate girder

A_B = area of rolled steel beam

A_c = transformed effective area of concrete slab = bt/kn

A_c' = transformed effective area of cracked slab = $y_{cc}b/kn$

A_{Ds} = steel area required to resist dead loads acting on the steel section alone

A_{Dc} = steel area required to resist dead loads acting on the composite section

A_{LL} = steel area required to resist live loads

A_p = area of steel cover plate

A_s = total area of steel section

A_t = area of top flange of plate girder

A_w = web area of steel section; also, weld area per inch of weld

b = effective width of concrete slab or distance shown in Fig. 2-8 or 2-9

b' = width of top flange of steel beam

C_L = M_L/wL^2

C_{mc} = ratio of maximum moment caused by dead loads acting on the composite section to maximum moment caused by live load = M_{Dc}/M_{LL}

C_{mi} = ratio of maximum moment caused by dead loads acting on steel beam alone to maximum moment caused by live load = M_{Ds}/M_{LL}

C_R = M_R/wL^2

C_s = ratio of section modulus of outermost bottom steel fiber of composite section to section modulus of outermost bottom steel fiber of the steel section = S_{bc}/S_{bs}

C_v = ratio of vertical shear caused by dead loads acting on composite section to vertical shear caused by live load = V_{Dc}/V_{LL}

d = depth of rolled steel beam or plate girder

d_s = stud diameter

d_{sp} = diameter of the spiral bar

DLc = dead load on composite section

DLs = dead load on steel beam alone

d_w = depth of web of plate girder

e_c = distance from top surface of steel beam or girder to center of gravity of effective concrete slab

E_c = modulus of elasticity of concrete

E_s = modulus of elasticity of steel

f_a = allowable stress

f_b = stress at outermost bottom steel fiber

f_c = stress at outermost top concrete fiber

f_c' = 28-day compressive strength of 6- by 12-in. concrete cylinders

FS = factor of safety

f_t = stress at outermost top steel fiber

f_w = allowable stress in weld

h = maximum thickness of channel flange

h_s = stud height

I = moment of inertia

I_b = moment of inertia of bottom flange of plate girder

I_B = moment of inertia of rolled steel beam

I_c = moment of inertia of composite section

I_p = moment of inertia of cover plate

I_s = moment of inertia of steel section

I_t = moment of inertia of top flange of plate girder

I_w = moment of inertia of web of plate girder

k = numerical factor depending on the type of loading; for temporary loads $k = k_{LL} = 1$, and for sustained loads $k = k_{Dc} = 3$

$$K_b = \frac{1 + 2(A_b/A_w)}{1 + (A_b/A_w) + (A_t/A_w)}$$

$$K_c = \frac{A_c}{A_c + A_s}$$

$$K_s = \frac{A_p}{A_s}$$

$$K_t = \frac{1 + 2(A_t/A_w)}{1 + (A_b/A_w) + (A_t/A_w)}$$

L = span length

L_{cp} = theoretical length of cover plate

L_w = total length of weld

LL = live load on composite section

LLFS = live-load factor of safety

m = statical moment of transformed compressive concrete area about neutral axis of composite section

M = moment

M_c = moment acting on composite section

M_{Dc} = dead-load moment acting on composite section

M_{Ds} = dead-load moment acting on steel section alone

M_L = restraining moment at left beam support

M_{LL} = live-load moment

M_R = restraining moment at right beam support

M_s = moment acting on steel section alone

M'_{Ds} = moment due to noncomposite dead load at end of cover plate

n = modular ratio E_s/E_c

N = number of studs in one row

p = spacing, or pitch, of rows of studs

P_L = one-half the weight of concentrated lane load for moment multiplied by distribution factor plus impact

P_T = weight of one front truck wheel multiplied by distribution factor plus impact

Q = resistance value of one shear connector at working load

Q_{uc} = useful capacity of shear connector

S = horizontal shear at junction of slab and beam

S_{cc} = section modulus of outermost concrete fiber for composite section

S_{bc} = section modulus of outermost bottom steel fiber for composite section

S_{bs} = section modulus of outermost bottom steel fiber for steel section

S_s = section modulus of outermost bottom and top steel fiber for symmetrical steel section

S_{tc} = section modulus of outermost top steel fiber for composite section

S_{ts} = section modulus of outermost top steel fiber for steel section

S'_{bc} = section modulus for bottom flange of composite section without cover plate in beam with cover plate cut off some distance from support

S'_{bs} = section modulus for bottom flange of rolled beam alone in beam with cover plate cut off some distance from support

t = thickness of concrete slab or thickness of web of channel connector

t_b = thickness of bottom steel flange of plate girder

t_p = thickness of bottom steel cover plate on rolled beam

t_t = thickness of top steel flange of plate girder

t_w = thickness of web of plate girder

u = average bond stress at contact surface of steel beam and concrete slab

V = total vertical shear

V_c = vertical shear acting on composite section

V_{Dc} = vertical dead-load shear acting on composite section

V_{Ds} = vertical dead-load shear acting on steel section alone

V_{LL} = vertical live-load shear

w = dead load or width of channel connector

w_L = one-half the weight of uniform lane load multiplied by distribution factor plus impact

y_{bc} = distance from neutral axis of composite section to outermost bottom steel fiber

y_{bs} = distance from neutral axis of steel section to outermost bottom steel fiber

y_{cc} = distance from neutral axis of composite section to outermost top concrete fiber

y_{cs} = distance from neutral axis of steel section to outermost top concrete fiber

y_{tc} = distance from neutral axis of composite section to outermost top steel fiber

y_{ts} = distance from neutral axis of steel section to outermost
top steel fiber

$\bar{y}_c$ = shift in neutral axis from addition of concrete slab

$\bar{y}_s$ = shift in neutral axis from addition of steel cover plate

Δ_{aL} = deflection at distance of aL from left support

Δ = deflection at mid-span

$\Delta_{0.4}$ = deflection at distance of $0.4L$ from simple support

CHAPTER 1

BASIC CONCEPTS IN COMPOSITE DESIGN

The slab-and-stringer bridge with a reinforced concrete slab as the roadway is one of the most common types in highway construction. It derives its popularity from its relatively low cost, ease and speed of construction, clean appearance, and simplicity of design.

Such a bridge is composed of two principal load-carrying elements: (1) the steel beams which transfer the loads in the direction along the bridge axis and (2) the concrete slab which distributes the loads in the transverse direction. However, if the slab is connected to the steel beams so that it cannot deform independently, it acts as a cover plate of the beams and assists the beams in carrying the loads in the longitudinal direction. The resulting structure is known as a composite slab-and-stringer bridge.

1-1. History of Composite Construction

The beginnings of composite construction in steel and concrete may be traced to the patent "Composite Beam Construction" issued to J. Kahn in 1926 and to the early studies of R. A. Caughey published in 1929. Several highway bridges of composite construction were built in the thirties and early forties.

The first specification for design of composite highway bridges, published by the American Association of State Highway Officials (AASHO) in 1944, represents a milestone in the development of this type of construction. The presentation of design principles in the specification undoubtedly implemented the rapid spread of composite bridges in the late forties. Systematic research studies and the vast amount of experience accumulated in the following decade proved the soundness of the basic principles but also indicated a need for more detailed provisions. Accordingly, the

1

AASHO published in 1957 a new, substantially expanded version of the specification for design of composite bridges. The provisions of the new specifications are followed in this book.

1-2. Advantages of Composite Construction

A composite structure is stronger and stiffer than a noncomposite structure made up of the same beams and slab. Thus composite design makes possible (1) savings in steel, (2) decrease in beam depth, or (3) economical use of rolled sections for longer spans.

These advantages of composite construction become especially pronounced if the noncomposite design is governed by deflection limitations. In addition, composite structures possess overload capacity and toughness substantially in excess of the overload capacity and toughness of noncomposite structures.

1-3. Elements of a Composite Beam

To secure interaction between the concrete slab and the steel beams, small pieces of steel bars or shapes are welded to the top flanges of the steel beams and embedded in the slab concrete. The function of these connectors is to transfer horizontal shear from the slab to the beams and thus to force the concrete and steel parts to act as a unit. Therefore composite slab-and-stringer construction is composed of three essential elements: (1) a reinforced concrete slab, (2) steel beams, and (3) shear connectors.

1. The *reinforced concrete slab* acts as a very effective cover plate if located on the compression side of the steel beams. The slab dimensions are generally dictated by the beam spacing and the required capacity for load transfer in the transverse direction. The design of the slab is independent of the composite action. It is carried out in the same manner as for noncomposite slab-and-stringer construction.

2. The *steel beams* may be rolled beams, rolled beams with cover plates, or built-up sections. Unsymmetrical beams, such as rolled beams with cover plates on the bottom flange, may be found economical for composite construction. Their design is explained in detail in Chap. 2.

3. *Shear connectors* provide the necessary connection between the slab and the beams. Shear connectors must be capable of

Dual bridges on south San Francisco highway are supported on girders of composite construction, the concrete deck acting as part of the top flange of the steel members.

transferring horizontal shear with very small deformations, i.e. with no appreciable slip between beams and slab, so that the whole structure deforms as a unit.   The design of shear connectors is presented in Chap. 3.

1-4. Methods of Constructing Composite Beams

A composite beam may be built with or without temporary supports (shoring).   When shores are not used, the steel beams support their own weight, the forms, and the weight of the slab during casting and curing of the slab.   Only the loads applied after the slab has hardened are resisted by the composite section.

When the steel beams rest on temporary supports until the slab concrete has attained the required strength, it may be assumed that all loads are carried by the composite section. Shored construction requires smaller steel sections than unshored construction.   However, *this economy in materials results in a smaller overload capacity* and is often offset by the cost of shoring. Furthermore, shoring is a delicate operation, especially if settlement of the temporary supports is difficult to prevent, which is usually the case in bridge construction.

CHAPTER 2

COMPOSITE BEAMS

2-1. Design Assumptions

For design purposes, a composite-deck structure is assumed to consist of a series of T beams, each made up of one steel beam and a portion of the concrete slab. The width of slab assumed effective as the flange of the T beam (except edge beams) must not exceed any of the following:

1. One-fourth of the span of the beam
2. The distance center to center of beams
3. Twelve times the least thickness of the slab

The flange of an edge beam is divided by the steel beam into two parts—inside and outside. The effective width of either part must not exceed one-twelfth of the span of the beam or six times the slab thickness. In addition, the effective width of the inside part must not exceed one-half the distance center to center of the beams, and the effective width of the outside part must not exceed the actual width.

Assuming further that shear connectors between steel beam and concrete slab do not permit any relative movement between the beam and slab, the T beams may be designed by the theory of transformed section. It is usually most convenient to transform the effective cross-sectional area of the concrete slab into an equivalent steel area. This is done by dividing the effective slab area by the modular ratio n. The remainder of the design calculations is then carried out as for a monolithic section. The calculated stresses must not exceed the allowable values for the respective materials.

2-2. Loading Conditions

Three types of loads must be considered in the design of composite T beams: (1) live loads, (2) dead loads (including shoring), and (3) deformational loads. Creep (plastic flow), shrinkage, expansion of concrete, and differential temperature changes are the deformations that may cause stresses in composite T beams; of these, shrinkage, expansion of concrete, and differential temperature changes need be considered only in exceptional cases.

2-3. Live Load

The principal live loads on highway bridges are the truck wheel loads. The concrete slab distributes the wheel loads transversely to several beams, so that one T beam may carry more or less than one wheel load. The distribution factors accounting for this action are given in the AASHO specifications.

For longer bridges, equivalent uniformly distributed lane loads with one concentrated load are often used in place of the wheel loads. Regardless of which type of loading is selected, the live load for bridges must include an allowance for impact.

In buildings, live loads generally are considered uniformly distributed.

The live loads are always carried by the composite section. They are usually of short duration. Thus, when the live-load stresses are computed, the properties of the composite section should be evaluated with the effective concrete area transformed by dividing only by the modular ratio $n = E_s/E_c$. Long-term loading, such as live loads in warehouses and from storage tanks, involves the use of a multiplier for n (Art. 2-4).

2-4. Dead Load, Shoring, and Creep

The steel beams, concrete slab, diaphragms, wearing surface, and other parts of the bridge superstructure constitute the dead loads. All dead loads placed on the bridge after the concrete slab has attained at least 75 per cent of its 28-day strength may be assumed to be carried by the composite section. In unshored construction, all other dead loads should be considered in the design as carried by the steel beams alone. In shored construction, these other dead loads are carried in part by shoring and in part by the steel beams. Upon shore removal the part carried by shoring is transferred to the composite section.

If at least three shores (at the quarter points) are provided between the end supports of a span, it is sufficiently accurate for design purposes to assume that all dead loads are carried by the composite section and to neglect the shoring.

Dead loads are permanent loads. Those acting on the composite section set up stresses in the concrete slab that cause the concrete to creep. The effect of creep is to relieve the stresses in the concrete and to increase the stresses in the steel beams. The effects of creep on the steel stresses may be accounted for approximately by multiplying the modular ratio $n = E_s/E_c$ by a numerical factor $k = 3$ in computing the stresses due to dead loads carried by the composite section.

The stress decrease in the slab due to creep and the corresponding stress increase in the bottom flange of the steel beam amount to only a few per cent of the total stress. On the other hand, the increase of stresses in the top flange of the steel beam may be significantly large.

2-5. Shrinkage

During the first several months after construction, the concrete slab shrinks. The shrinkage sets up tensile stresses in the slab, compressive stresses in the top flange of the steel beam, and tensile stresses in the bottom flange. If the tensile stresses in the slab exceed the tensile strength of concrete, cracks form and the slab becomes ineffective in resisting stresses. In simple beams and in the positive-moment regions of continuous beams, load deformations close the shrinkage cracks and thus restore the effectiveness of the slab in resisting compressive stresses. In negative-moment regions of continuous beams, however, the loads cause further opening of cracks, so that in these regions shrinkage cracking makes the slab permanently ineffective in resisting stresses.

Shrinkage is a long-time phenomenon. Thus the shrinkage stresses in the slab of a composite T beam are accompanied by time-dependent permanent deformations of concrete; in other words, relaxation[1] takes place. Accordingly, the shrinkage stresses may be computed either on the basis of the usual free shrinkage or on the basis of a smaller unit shrinkage (free shrinkage corrected for the effects of relaxation). In the first method, the effects of relaxation must be considered, e.g., by using $k = 3$ (see Art. 2-4). In the second method the effects of relaxation are

[1] Relaxation is a phenomenon similar to creep.

included in the coefficient of unit shrinkage; therefore, computations of stresses should be based on $k = 1$. The second method was selected for this book.

Tests of composite T beams have indicated that the unit shrinkage of the slab of a composite beam may be assumed equal to 0.0002 in. per in. The corresponding stresses may be computed on the basis of one of the following two assumptions:

1. The shrinkage does not cause cracking. In this case, the slab is in tension and the steel stresses can be evaluated by considering the composite cross section as an eccentrically loaded column with a load of $0.0002E_c n A_c$ applied at the centroid of the slab and using $n = E_s/E_c$ (that is, $k = 1$).

2. The shrinkage causes cracking of the slab. The total opening of shrinkage cracks is equal to the unit shrinkage multiplied by the length of the beam. To close the cracks, the stress in the top flange of the steel beam must equal the noncomposite dead-load stress plus $0.0002E_s$.

Calculations for typical composite beams have shown that the differences between the steel stresses computed from the two different assumptions are negligible. Furthermore, the calculations have shown that the shrinkage stresses in the bottom flange are always substantially less than the AASHO allowable 25 per cent overstress for group loadings. The maximum top-flange stress in unsymmetrical steel sections may, in some exceptional cases, exceed slightly the allowable 25 per cent overstress.

The shrinkage stresses in the slabs of simple beams and in the positive-moment regions of continuous beams are counteracted by the dead- and live-load stresses. In the negative-moment regions of continuous beams, the shrinkage stresses in the slab are unimportant, since the slab is considered ineffective in resisting tensile stresses. Accordingly, the effect of shrinkage on the slab stresses may ordinarily be neglected in the design.

2-6. Design of Composite Beams

The following design of composite beams is based on allowable stresses for the component materials. It consists of selecting the cross section and of computing stresses at various locations.

For structures with wide-flange beams, the selection may be done with the aid of Table 5-2, containing the section moduli for the wide-flange beams alone and in combination with slabs of

various dimensions. Values intermediate between those listed
in the table may be obtained by straight-line interpolation. If
the effects of concrete haunch between the slab and the steel
beam and the effects of creep and shrinkage are neglected, the
bottom-flange stress in the beam may be expressed as follows:

$$f_b = \frac{M_{Ds}}{S_{bs}} + \frac{M_{Dc} + M_{LL}}{S_{bc}}$$

where the section modulus of the composite section S_{bc}, relative
to the steel-beam bottom flange, is based on $n = E_s/E_c$; that is,
$k = 1$ (see Art. 2-4); S_{bs} = section modulus of steel section relative to the bottom flange; M_{Ds} = dead-load moment in the steel
beam; M_{Dc} = dead-load moment in the composite section; and
M_{LL} = live-load moment. The stress equation may be rewritten
in the following form:

$$S_{bc} = \frac{S_{bc}}{S_{bs}}\frac{M_{Ds}}{f_b} + \frac{M_{Dc} + M_{LL}}{f_b}$$

The ratio S_{bc}/S_{bs} can be found approximately from Table 5-2.[1]
As M_{Ds}/f_b and $(M_{Dc} + M_{LL})/f_b$ are known quantities, the necessary section modulus of the composite section can be computed
approximately from the equation above and the corresponding
beam section found in Table 5-2. The method is illustrated in
Example 2-1, Method A, in Art. 2-11.

Unsymmetrical steel sections, such as a rolled beam with a
cover plate on the bottom flange (see Fig. 2-1) or a built-up plate
girder (see Fig. 2-2), are more suitable for composite construction than symmetrical rolled sections. The selection of such
cross sections may be made by the trial method discussed in
Arts. 2-12 and 2-13.

After the cross section has been selected, stresses are computed
in the bottom and top fibers of the steel section and in the top
fibers of the concrete slab. The stresses are computed for each
type of loading, i.e., for the live load including impact, composite
dead load including creep, and noncomposite dead load carried
by the steel beam alone. The total stress at any location is the
algebraic sum of the stresses due to individual types of loading.
The total stress must not exceed the allowable value.

[1] For symmetrical steel sections such as WF beams, $S_{bs} = S_{ts} = S_s$.

In bridge construction, the concrete slab usually does not rest directly on the top flange of the I beam (Fig. 2-3). Instead, a concrete haunch or fillet is inserted between the slab proper and the beam. The contribution of this haunch to the load-resisting capacity of the composite section is very small. To avoid unnecessary complexity, the contribution of the haunch is neglected in the following formulas for the properties of composite sections.

2-7. Formulas for Dead- and Live-load Stresses

Flexural stresses due to dead and live loads can be computed by the moment-of-inertia method. When the moment of inertia of the composite section is computed, the concrete on the compression side of the neutral axis is transformed into an equivalent steel area and the concrete on the tension side of the neutral axis is considered ineffective. The compressive area of the concrete slab may then be treated in the same manner as a steel cover plate.

A portion or all of the dead load is usually carried by the steel section alone. If the steel section consists of a rolled beam with a steel cover plate on the bottom flange (Fig. 2-1), the corresponding stresses may be computed from the following formulas:

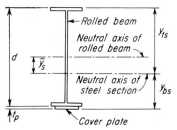

Fig. 2-1. Rolled beam with cover plate.

$$K_s = \frac{A_p}{A_s} \tag{2-1a}$$

$$\bar{y}_s = \tfrac{1}{2}(d + t_p)K_s \tag{2-1b}$$

$$I_s = \tfrac{1}{2}(d + t_p)\bar{y}_s A_B + I_B \qquad \text{(small quantity } I_p \text{ neglected)} \tag{2-1c}$$

$$y_{ts} = \frac{d}{2} + \bar{y}_s \tag{2-1d}$$

$$y_{bs} = \frac{d}{2} + t_p - \bar{y}_s \tag{2-1e}$$

$$f_t = \frac{M_s y_{ts}}{I_s} = \frac{M_s}{S_{ts}} \tag{2-1f}$$

$$f_b = \frac{M_s y_{bs}}{I_s} = \frac{M_s}{S_{bs}} \tag{2-1g}$$

If the steel section consists of an unsymmetrical welded plate
girder (Fig. 2-2), the following formulas apply:

$$\bar{y}_s = \frac{\tfrac{1}{2}(d_w + t_b)A_b - \tfrac{1}{2}(d_w + t_t)A_t}{A_s} \tag{2-2a}$$

$$I_s = \tfrac{1}{4}(d_w + t_t)^2 A_t + \tfrac{1}{4}(d_w + t_b)^2 A_b + I_w - A_s(\bar{y}_s)^2$$
$$\text{(small quantities } I_t \text{ and } I_b \text{ neglected)} \tag{2-2b}$$

$$y_{ts} = \tfrac{1}{2}d_w + t_t + \bar{y}_s \tag{2-2c}$$

$$y_{bs} = \tfrac{1}{2}d_w + t_b - \bar{y}_s \tag{2-2d}$$

$$f_t = \frac{M_s y_{ts}}{I_s} = \frac{M_s}{S_{ts}} \tag{2-2e}$$

$$f_b = \frac{M_s y_{bs}}{I_s} = \frac{M_s}{S_{bs}} \tag{2-2f}$$

A portion or all of the dead loads and all live loads are carried
by the composite section. The properties of the composite section are a function of the product of the modular ratio n and a
numerical factor k. The factor k is used to account for the
effects of creep. For loads of short duration, such as live loads
for bridges, no creep effects are present ($k = 1$); for sustained
loads, such as dead loads, the effects of creep may be accounted
for by using $k = 3$.

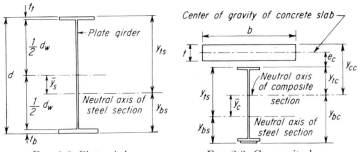

FIG. 2-2. Plate girder.   FIG. 2-3. Composite beam.

In composite sections, the neutral axis may be located either
below or in the slab. If it is located below the slab (Fig. 2-3), the
full cross section of the slab is effective in resisting the stresses,
and the stresses can be computed from the following formulas:

$$n = \frac{E_s}{E_c} \tag{2-3a}$$

k = numerical factor, depending on type of loading, equal
to 1 for temporary loads and 3 for sustained loads $\qquad$ (2-3b)

$$A_c = \frac{bt}{kn} \qquad (2\text{-}3c)$$

$$K_c = \frac{A_c}{A_c + A_s} \qquad (2\text{-}3d)$$

$$\bar{y}_c = (y_{ts} + e_c)K_c \qquad (2\text{-}3e)$$

$$I_c = (y_{ts} + e_c)\bar{y}_c A_s + I_s + A_c \frac{t^2}{12} \qquad (2\text{-}3f)$$

$$y_{tc} = y_{ts} - \bar{y}_c \qquad (2\text{-}3g)$$

$$y_{bc} = y_{bs} + \bar{y}_c \qquad (2\text{-}3h)$$

$$y_{cc} = y_{tc} + e_c + \frac{t}{2} \qquad (2\text{-}3i)$$

$$m = A_c(y_{tc} + e_c) \qquad (2\text{-}3j)$$

$$f_t = \frac{M_c y_{tc}}{I_c} = \frac{M_c}{S_{tc}} \qquad (2\text{-}3k)$$

$$f_b = \frac{M_c y_{bc}}{I_c} = \frac{M_c}{S_{bc}} \qquad (2\text{-}3l)$$

$$f_c = \frac{M_c y_{cc}}{kn I_c} = \frac{M_c}{kn S_{cc}} \qquad (2\text{-}3m)$$

If the neutral axis is located in the slab, only the portion of the slab above the neutral axis is considered effective in resisting stresses. However, studies have shown that Eqs. (2-3) give sufficiently accurate results even if the neutral axis is located in the slab as long as the following condition is satisfied:

$$\frac{d}{t} \geqq \frac{1}{3}\frac{A_c}{A_s}$$

This limitation is invariably satisfied in bridge design.

Equations (2-1), (2-2), and (2-3) are applicable also to beams with rolled sections without cover plates ($A_p = 0$) and to beams with symmetrical welded plate girders ($A_t = A_b$, $t_t = t_b$).

The vertical shear is usually assumed to be taken entirely by the web of the steel section. The effects of this shear are then calculated by the conventional methods for steel beams or girders. Thus the shearing stresses in the web may be computed as the ratio of the vertical shear V to the area of the web A_w.

2-8. Formulas for Shrinkage Stresses

Shrinkage stresses in the top and bottom steel flanges of a composite beam can be computed as the stresses in an eccentrically loaded column with a load of $0.0002\, E_c n A_c$ applied at the centroid of the slab. Noting that $n = E_s/E_c$, the stresses can be expressed as follows:

$$f_t = 0.0002 E_s \left(K_c + \frac{y_{cc} - \frac{1}{2}t}{S_{tc}/A_c} \right) \qquad \text{compression} \quad (2\text{-}4a)$$

$$f_b = 0.0002 E_s \left(-K_c + \frac{y_{cc} - \frac{1}{2}t}{S_{bc}/A_c} \right) \qquad \text{tension} \quad (2\text{-}4b)$$

When the properties of the composite cross section are computed, $k = 1$ should be used.

It should be noted that when shrinkage is considered in the design, the AASHO specifications permit a 25 per cent increase of allowable stresses. With this provision, shrinkage stresses ordinarily need not be considered in the design.

2-9. Selection of Cross Section of Rolled Beams and Cover Plates

It has been pointed out in the preceding section that shrinkage stresses ordinarily need not be considered in the design of composite beams. Thus the selection of a cross section may be made on the basis of dead and live loads (including impact) only. The dimensions of the slab are determined by the design for transverse load distribution and by the layout of the bridge; only the steel section need be determined by trial.

The trial procedure presented herein consists essentially of three steps: (1) assume a symmetrical steel section, (2) compute approximately the necessary steel area, and (3) revise the assumed steel section according to the computed steel area. The third step consists either of revising the whole section or of adding a cover plate on the tension side.

With the steel cross section selected, the stresses can be computed as outlined in the preceding section. Ordinarily, the resulting stresses will be close to the allowable values, so that no further revisions of the cross section are necessary.

2-10. Approximate Section Properties

A cross section composed of a concrete slab and a symmetrical steel beam is shown in Fig. 2-4. If the neutral axis of the composite section is located below the slab, the following properties of the composite section may be obtained from Eqs. (2-3):

$$\frac{\bar{y}_c}{d} = \left(\frac{1}{2} + \frac{e_c}{d}\right) K_c \tag{2-5a}$$

$$\frac{I_c}{A_s d^2} = \left(\frac{1}{2} + \frac{e_c}{d}\right)^2 K_c + \frac{I_s}{A_s d^2} + \frac{1}{12} \frac{A_c}{A_s}\left(\frac{t}{d}\right)^2 \tag{2-5b}$$

$$\frac{S_{bc}}{A_s d} = \frac{1}{\frac{1}{2} + (\bar{y}_c/d)} \frac{I_c}{A_s d^2} \qquad \frac{S_{tc}}{A_s d} = \frac{1}{\frac{1}{2} - (\bar{y}_c/d)} \frac{I_c}{A_s d^2} \tag{2-5c}$$

The quantity $\frac{1}{12}(A_c/A_s)(t/d)^2$ is relatively small and may be neglected in the preliminary calculations leading to selection of the cross section. The quantity $I_s/A_s d^2$ is the square of the ratio of the radius of gyration to the depth of the steel section. This ratio depends only on the shape of the cross section; for wide-flange beams it may be taken as 0.165:

$$\frac{I_s}{A_s d^2} \approx 0.165 \tag{2-6a}$$

and
$$\frac{S_{bs}}{A_s d} = \frac{S_{ts}}{A_s d} = \frac{S_s}{A_s d} = 2 \frac{I_s}{A_s d^2} \approx 0.33 \tag{2-6b}$$

Substitution into Eq. (2-5b) gives the following approximate expression:

$$\frac{I_c}{A_s d^2} \approx \left(\frac{1}{2} + \frac{e_c}{d}\right)^2 K_c + 0.165 \tag{2-6c}$$

The expressions for the section moduli for the bottom and top steel fibers may be expressed approximately as

$$\frac{S_{bc}}{A_s d} \approx \frac{1}{\frac{1}{2} + \left(\frac{1}{2} + \frac{e_c}{d}\right) K_c} \left[\left(\frac{1}{2} + \frac{e_c}{d}\right)^2 K_c + 0.165\right] \tag{2-6d}$$

$$\frac{S_{tc}}{A_s d} \approx \frac{1}{\frac{1}{2} - \left(\frac{1}{2} + \frac{e_c}{d}\right) K_c} \left[\left(\frac{1}{2} + \frac{e_c}{d}\right)^2 K_c + 0.165\right] \tag{2-6e}$$

where $K_c = A_c/(A_c + A_s)$.

It should be noted that the right-hand sides of Eqs. (2-6d) and (2-6e) are functions of e_c/d and K_c, which can be evaluated if the depth and area of the steel section are known approximately.

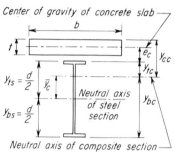

FIG. 2-4. Composite beam with symmetrical rolled section.

A graphical solution of Eq. (2-6d) is given in Fig. 5-1, and a graphical solution of Eq. (2-6e) is given in Fig. 5-2. The figures include several values of e_c/d covering the practical range; for intermediate values of e_c/d straight-line interpolation gives satisfactory results.

Figures 5-1 and 5-2 (or the corresponding equations) may be used in selection of the cross sections as is shown in the following articles.

2-11. Rolled Beams without Cover Plates

One method for selecting the necessary wide-flange section was presented in Art. 2-6. It is based on Table 5-2 and, therefore, limited to the rolled sections listed in that table. A more general method is presented here.

When the composite section consists of a slab and a symmetrical rolled steel beam, the size of the positive-moment section is governed by the bottom-flange stress given by the equation

$$f_b = \frac{M_{Ds}}{S_{bs}} + \frac{M_{Dc}}{S_{bc}} + \frac{M_{LL}}{S_{bc}} \tag{2-7a}$$

where M_{Ds} = moment caused by dead loads carried by steel section alone

M_{Dc} = moment caused by dead loads carried by composite section

M_{LL} = moment caused by live loads

Equation (2-7a) may be rewritten in the following form:

$$A_s = \frac{M_{Ds}}{f_b(S_{bs}/A_s d)d} + \frac{M_{Dc}}{f_b(S_{bc}/A_s d)d} + \frac{M_{LL}}{f_b(S_{bc}/A_s d)d} \tag{2-7b}$$

This gives the required total steel area A_s as a summation of three areas needed for the three types of loads. In the expressions for the component areas,

$$A_{Ds} = \frac{M_{Ds}}{f_b} \frac{A_s d}{S_{bs}} \frac{1}{d} \qquad A_{Dc} = \frac{M_{Dc}}{f_b} \frac{A_s d}{S_{bc}} \frac{1}{d} \qquad A_{LL} = \frac{M_{LL}}{f_b} \frac{A_s d}{S_{bc}} \frac{1}{d}$$

$$(2\text{-}7c)$$

the first term is the required section modulus for the particular type of moment, and the second term is one of the Eqs. (2-6) given in Art. 2-10. Thus, the necessary steel area can be computed as follows:

1. Compute the required section modulus for each type of loading.

2. Assume a steel area A_s and depth d of the rolled beam; it is usually sufficiently accurate to select a rolled beam two or three sizes smaller than that needed for a noncomposite T beam. With the assumed values of A_s and d and with the known values of e_c and A_c, compute e_c/d and K_c. The A_c value for composite dead loads is computed with $k = 3$ and for live loads with $k = 1$; thus two values of K_c are obtained.

3. From Fig. 5-1, get $S_{bc}/A_s d$ corresponding to the values e_c/d and K_c computed above. Either take $S_{bs}/A_s d$ as 0.33, or if a certain steel section was assumed in step 2, compute it for the assumed section with the aid of a handbook (values of S_s/A_s for some sections[1] are listed in the third column of Table 5-2).

4. Compute the necessary steel areas as

$$A_s = A_{Ds} + A_{Dc} + A_{LL} \qquad (2\text{-}7d)$$

Select a section having the assumed d and the required A_s.

If the required area differs substantially from the assumed area, it may be desirable to repeat the calculations. However, as long as the difference is no more than about 20 per cent, repetition of the calculations is usually unnecessary.

The procedure is illustrated in Method B of Example 2-1, which follows. The example includes also computation of stresses. The allowable stresses are $f'_c = 1,200$ psi with $n = 10$, and $f_t = f_b = 18,000$ psi.

Example 2-1. Design a rolled beam without cover plates for the composite beam shown in Fig. 2-5, which is not to be shored

[1] Since this article involves a rolled beam with no cover plates, $A_s = A_B$.

when the slab is concreted.   Moments are as follows:

$$M_{Ds} = 300 \text{ kip-ft}$$
$$M_{Dc} = 180 \text{ kip-ft}$$
$$M_{LL} = 430 \text{ kip-ft}$$

Determine for each moment the required section modulus for a noncomposite beam:

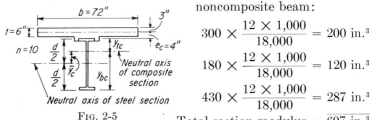

FIG. 2-5

$$300 \times \frac{12 \times 1,000}{18,000} = 200 \text{ in.}^3$$

$$180 \times \frac{12 \times 1,000}{18,000} = 120 \text{ in.}^3$$

$$430 \times \frac{12 \times 1,000}{18,000} = 287 \text{ in.}^3$$

$$\text{Total section modulus} = \overline{607 \text{ in.}^3}$$

Example 2-1.   Method A.   Since the total required section modulus is 607 in.³, a 36 WF 182 would be necessary for a noncomposite structure (Table 5-2).   A composite structure will require a steel beam approximately three sizes smaller.   Thus, moving three spaces lower in the table to 36 WF 150 and selecting the section modulus for this section with and without a 6-in. slab of 6-ft. flange width, we can compute

$$\frac{S_{bc}}{S_{bs}} \approx \frac{661.4}{502.9} = 1.31$$

Now, since the steel section alone needs a section modulus of 200 for dead load, the composite section must have a section modulus for the same load of 1.31 × 200.   Then the total section modulus for the composite beam must be

$$S_{bc} \approx 1.31 \times 200 + 120 + 287 = 669 \text{ in.}^3$$

Try a 36 WF 150 with $S_{bc} = 661.4$ in.³.

Example 2-1.   Method B.   Assume a 36 WF 150 with $A_s = 44.16$ in.², $d = 35.84$ in., $I_s = 9,012$ in.⁴, $S_s = 502.9$ in.³.

$$\frac{e_c}{d} = \frac{4}{35.84} = 0.11 \qquad\qquad \frac{S_s}{A_s} = \frac{502.9}{44.16} = 11.39 \text{ in.}$$

$$k_{Dc} = 3 \qquad\qquad\qquad\qquad k_{LL} = 1$$

$$A_c = \frac{bt}{kn} = \frac{72 \times 6}{3 \times 10} = 14.4 \text{ in.}^2 \qquad A_c = \frac{72 \times 6}{1 \times 10} = 43.2 \text{ in.}^2$$

$$K_c = \frac{A_c}{A_c + A_s} = \frac{14.4}{14.4 + 44.16} \qquad K_c = \frac{43.2}{43.2 + 44.16}$$

$$= 0.246 \qquad\qquad\qquad\qquad = 0.495$$

From Fig. 5-1, for $k = 3$ and 1, respectively,

$$\frac{S_{bc}}{A_s d} = 0.396 \qquad \frac{S_{bc}}{A_s d} = 0.437$$

Trial Section. Applying Eq. (2-7c), we compute the required area of the steel section.

Bottom flange:

$$A_{Ds} = \frac{M_{Ds}/f_b}{S_s/A_s} = \frac{200}{11.39} = 17.56 \text{ in.}^2$$

$$A_{Dc} = \frac{M_{Dc}}{f_b} \frac{A_s d}{S_{bc}} \frac{1}{d} = \frac{120}{0.396 \times 35.84} = 8.46$$

$$A_{LL} = \frac{M_{LL}}{f_b} \frac{A_s d}{S_{bc}} \frac{1}{d} = \frac{287}{0.437 \times 35.84} = 18.32$$

$$A_s = \overline{44.34 \text{ in.}^2}$$

compared with the 44.16 in.² area of a 36 WF 150; therefore, a 36 WF 150 is suitable (as found also by Method A).

Properties of Trial Section [Eqs. (2-3)]

Composite section with $k = 3$:

$$K_c = \frac{A_c}{A_c + A_s} = 0.246$$

$$\bar{y}_c = (y_{ts} + e_c)K_c = (17.92 + 4)0.246 = 5.39 \text{ in.}$$

$$I_c = (y_{ts} + e_c)\bar{y}_c A_s + I_s + A_c \frac{t^2}{12} = 21.92 \times 5.39 \times 44.16$$

$$+ 9{,}012 + \frac{14.4 \times 6^2}{12} = 14{,}270 \text{ in.}^4$$

$$y_{tc} = y_{ts} - \bar{y}_c = 17.92 - 5.39 = 12.53 \text{ in.}$$

$$S_{tc} = \frac{I_c}{y_{tc}} = 1{,}139 \text{ in.}^3$$

$$y_{bc} = y_{bs} + \bar{y}_c = 17.92 + 5.39 = 23.31 \text{ in.}$$

$$S_{bc} = \frac{I_c}{y_{bc}} = 612 \text{ in.}^3$$

$$y_{cc} = y_{tc} + e_c + \frac{t}{2} = 12.53 + 4 + 3 = 19.53 \text{ in.}$$

$$S_{cc} = \frac{I_c}{y_{cc}} = 730 \text{ in.}^3$$

Composite section with $k = 1$:

$$K_c = 0.495$$

$$\bar{y}_c = (21.92)0.495 = 10.84 \text{ in.}$$

$$I_c = 10.84 \times 21.92 \times 44.16 + 9{,}012 + \frac{43.2 \times 6^2}{12} = 19{,}630 \text{ in.}^4$$

$y_{tc} = 17.92 - 10.84 = 7.08$ in.

$S_{tc} = 2{,}770$ in.^{3}

$y_{bc} = 17.92 + 10.84 = 28.76$ in.

$S_{bc} = 682$ in.^{3}

$y_{cc} = 7.08 + 4 + 3 = 14.08$ in.

$S_{cc} = 1{,}394$ in.^{3}

Stresses

	Concrete, f_c, ksi	Steel top flange, f_t, ksi	Steel bottom flange, f_b, ksi
Dead load on steel beam alone (DLs)	0	$\dfrac{300 \times 12}{502.9} = 7.16$	$\dfrac{300 \times 12}{502.9} = 7.16$
Dead load on composite section (DLc)	$\dfrac{180 \times 12}{730 \times 30} = 0.10$	$\dfrac{180 \times 12}{1{,}139} = 1.90$	$\dfrac{180 \times 12}{612} = 3.53$
Live load on composite section (LL)	$\dfrac{430 \times 12}{1{,}394 \times 10} = 0.37$	$\dfrac{430 \times 12}{2{,}770} = 1.86$	$\dfrac{430 \times 12}{682} = 7.56$
	0.47	10.92	18.25

2-12. Rolled Beams with Cover Plates

Composite beams usually incorporate an unsymmetrical steel section, such as a rolled beam with a cover plate on the tension flange or an unsymmetrical plate girder. The selection of such sections is governed by the bottom-flange (tension) and top-flange (compression) steel stress. If the steel beam is made up of a rolled section and a cover plate, the size of the rolled section is usually selected on the basis of the top-flange stress; the size of the cover plate is selected on the basis of the bottom-flange stress.

It may be shown by a procedure similar to that given in Art. 2-11 that the necessary symmetrical beam area may be computed on the basis of the top-flange stress as

$$A_B = A_{Ds} + A_{Dc} + A_{LL} \qquad (2\text{-}8a)$$

where

$$A_{Ds} = \frac{M_{Ds}}{f_t} \frac{A_s d}{S_{ts}} \frac{1}{d} \qquad A_{Dc} = \frac{M_{Dc}}{f_t} \frac{A_s d}{S_{tc}} \frac{1}{d} \qquad A_{LL} = \frac{M_{LL}}{f_t} \frac{A_s d}{S_{tc}} \frac{1}{d}$$
$$(2\text{-}8b)$$

The beam section is selected in the same way as described in Art. 2-11, except that the required beam area is based on the

Steel girders of the Crawford-Elysian Street overpass, Houston, Tex., are shown ready to receive the concrete deck. Studs welded to the top flanges assure composite action between steel and concrete.

stress in the top flange, requiring the use of Fig. 5-2 instead of Fig. 5-1. The size of the rolled beam is usually four or more sizes smaller than that needed for a noncomposite beam.

The area of the cover plate is found by computing the area A_s of a symmetrical beam corresponding to the allowable bottom-flange stress. Then the difference $A_s - A_B$ corresponds to the increase in the symmetrical section over that necessary for the top-flange stress. The area A_p of one cover plate can be computed as follows:

$$A_p = \tfrac{1}{2}(A_s - A_B) \quad (2\text{-}9)$$

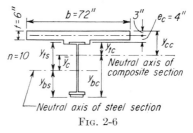

Fig. 2-6

The procedure for selecting the cross section for a composite beam composed of a slab and a rolled beam with cover plate is illustrated in Example 2-2. The allowable stresses are the same as for Example 2-1 (Art. 2-11).

Example 2-2. Design an unshored rolled beam with a cover plate for the composite beam shown in Fig. 2-6. Moments and partial section moduli are the same as in Example 2-1.

Moments, kip-ft	Section modulus, in.³
$M_{Ds} = 300$	200
$M_{Dc} = 180$	120
$M_{LL} = 430$	287

Assume a 30 WF 108, with area $A_B = 31.77$ in.², depth $d = 29.82$ in., moment of inertia $I_B = 4,461$ in.⁴, and section modulus $S_B = 299.2$ in.³.

$$\frac{e_c}{d} = \frac{4}{29.82} = 0.13 \qquad \frac{S_B}{A_B} = \frac{299.2}{31.77} = 9.42 \text{ in.}$$

$$k_{Dc} = 3 \qquad\qquad\qquad k_{LL} = 1$$

$$A_c = \frac{bt}{kn} = \frac{72 \times 6}{3 \times 10} = 14.4 \text{ in.}^2 \qquad A_c = \frac{72 \times 6}{1 \times 10} = 43.2 \text{ in.}^2$$

$$K_c = \frac{A_c}{A_c + A_s} = \frac{14.4}{14.4 + 31.77} \qquad K_c = \frac{43.2}{43.2 + 31.77}$$
$$= 0.312 \qquad\qquad\qquad = 0.576$$

From Figs. 5-1 and 5-2, for $k = 3$ and 1, respectively,

$$\frac{S_{bc}}{A_s d} = 0.416 \qquad \frac{S_{bc}}{A_s d} = 0.459$$

$$\frac{A_s d}{S_{tc}} = 1.04 \qquad \frac{A_s d}{S_{tc}} = 0.35$$

Trial Section. Substituting in Eqs. (2-8), we find the required areas of the steel section.

Top flange:

$$A_{Ds} = \frac{200}{9.42} \qquad\qquad = \quad 21.23 \text{ in.}^2$$

$$A_{Dc} = \frac{120 \times 1.04}{29.82} \qquad = \quad 4.19$$

$$A_{LL} = \frac{287 \times 0.35}{29.82} \qquad = \quad 3.37$$

$$\text{Required } A_B = \quad \overline{28.79 \text{ in.}^2}$$
$$A_B = \quad 31.77$$

Bottom flange:

$$A_{Ds} = \frac{200}{9.42} \qquad\qquad = \quad 21.23 \text{ in.}^2$$

$$A_{Dc} = \frac{120}{0.416 \times 29.82} \qquad = \quad 9.67$$

$$A_{LL} = \frac{287}{0.459 \times 29.82} \qquad = \quad 20.97$$

$$A_s = \quad \overline{51.87 \text{ in.}^2}$$
$$A_B = \quad -31.77$$
$$\overline{20.10 \text{ in.}^2}$$

From Eq. 2-9, the required $A_p = 20.10/2 = 10.05$ in.².
Try 8 by 1¼ plate; $A_p = 10.00$ in.².

Properties of Trial Section

Steel section [from (Eq. 2-1)]:

$$K_s = \frac{A_p}{A_s} = \frac{10.00}{10.00 + 31.77} = 0.239$$

$$\bar{y}_s = \frac{1}{2}(d + t_p)K_s = \frac{1}{2}(29.82 + 1.25)0.239 = 3.72 \text{ in.}$$

$$I_s = \frac{1}{2}(d + t_p)\bar{y}_s A_B + I_B = \frac{1}{2} \times 31.07 \times 3.72 \times 31.77$$
$$+ 4{,}461 = 6{,}297 \text{ in.}^4$$

$$y_{ts} = \frac{d}{2} + \bar{y}_s = 14.91 + 3.72 = 18.63 \text{ in.}$$

$$S_{ts} = \frac{I_s}{y_{ts}} = 338 \text{ in.}^3$$

$$y_{bs} = \frac{d}{2} + t_p - \bar{y}_s = 14.91 + 1.25 - 3.72 = 12.44 \text{ in.}$$

$$S_{bs} = \frac{I_s}{y_{bs}} = 506 \text{ in.}^3$$

Composite section [from (Eq. 2-3)] with $k = 3$:

$$K_c = \frac{A_c}{A_c + A_s} = \frac{14.4}{14.4 + 41.77} = 0.256$$

$$\bar{y}_c = (y_{ts} + e_c)K_c = (18.63 + 4)0.256 = 5.80 \text{ in.}$$

$$I_c = (y_{ts} + e_c)\bar{y}_c A_s + I_s + A_c \frac{t^2}{12} = 22.63 \times 5.80 \times 41.77$$
$$+ 6{,}297 + \frac{14.4 \times 6^2}{12} = 11{,}820 \text{ in.}^4$$

$$y_{tc} = y_{ts} - \bar{y}_c = 18.63 - 5.80 = 12.83 \text{ in.}$$

$$S_{tc} = \frac{I_c}{y_{tc}} = 921 \text{ in.}^3$$

$$y_{bc} = y_{bs} + \bar{y}_c = 12.44 + 5.80 = 18.24 \text{ in.}$$

$$S_{bc} = \frac{I_c}{y_{bc}} = 648 \text{ in.}^3$$

$$y_{cc} = y_{tc} + e_c + \frac{t}{2} = 12.83 + 4 + 3 = 19.83 \text{ in.}$$

$$S_{cc} = \frac{I_c}{y_{cc}} = 596 \text{ in.}^3$$

Composite section with $k = 1$:

$$K_c = \frac{43.2}{43.2 + 41.77} = 0.508$$

$$\bar{y}_c = 22.63 \times 0.508 = 11.51 \text{ in.}$$

$$I_c = 22.63 \times 11.51 \times 41.77 + 6{,}297 + \frac{43.2 \times 6^2}{12} = 17{,}310 \text{ in.}^4$$

$y_{tc} = 18.63 - 11.51 = 7.12$ in.

$S_{tc} = 2{,}430$ in.^{3}

$y_{bc} = 12.44 + 11.51 = 23.95$ in.

$S_{bc} = 723$ in.^{3}

$y_{cc} = 7.12 + 4 + 3 = 14.12$ in.

$S_{cc} = 1{,}226$ in.^{3}

Stresses

	f_c, ksi	f_t, ksi	f_b, ksi
DLs	0	$\dfrac{300 \times 12}{338} = 10.65$	$\dfrac{300 \times 12}{506} = 7.11$
DLc	$\dfrac{180 \times 12}{596 \times 30} = 0.12$	$\dfrac{180 \times 12}{921} = 2.34$	$\dfrac{180 \times 12}{648} = 3.33$
LL	$\dfrac{430 \times 12}{1{,}226 \times 10} = 0.42$	$\dfrac{430 \times 12}{2{,}430} = 2.12$	$\dfrac{430 \times 12}{723} = 7.14$
	0.54	15.11	17.58

The moments for Examples 2-1 and 2-2 are the same; therefore, the selected sections illustrate the difference in weights of an unsymmetrical composite section and symmetrical composite section. If the length of the cover plate for Example 2-2 is about ⅔ the total span, this section yields an average saving of 20 lb per ft of beam length, or 15 per cent, over the section of Example 2-1. Of course, this saving in material is achieved at an increased cost of fabrication.

The corresponding noncomposite section is a 36 WF 182. Thus the unsymmetrical composite section results in an average saving of 52 lb per ft of beam length, or 28 per cent, over the noncomposite section.

The required area of symmetrical section for the top flange of Example 2-2 is close to the actual section chosen, but the calculated top-flange stress is comparatively low. The top-flange stress is relatively sensitive to area variations, and small changes in area can produce large changes in stress as can be seen from Fig. 5-2. The preliminary design for this flange is not so accurate as the preliminary design for the bottom flange.

2-13. Welded Plate Girders

The selection of an unsymmetrical plate girder for a composite beam may be made by a method similar to that described in Arts. 2-11 and 2-12 for rolled beams. The trial procedure consists essentially of three steps: (1) assume the size of the web (i.e., depth and thickness) and the ratios of top flange to web area and of bottom flange to web area; (2) compute approximately the necessary steel area for the top and bottom flanges; and (3) revise the assumed ratios, repeat the calculations if necessary, and select the sizes of the top and bottom flanges.

The stresses in the selected cross section are then computed from the formulas in Arts. 2-7 and 2-8. Ordinarily, the resulting stresses will be close to the allowable values, so that no further revisions of the cross section are necessary.

The section properties of an unsymmetrical plate girder can be computed from Eqs. (2-2), and the section properties of the corresponding composite beam can be computed from Eqs. (2-3). Assuming that

$$d_w + t_b \approx d_w + t_t \approx d \approx d_w$$

the following approximate expression may be obtained from Eqs. (2-2) for the bottom- and top-flange section moduli S_{bs} and S_{ts} of the steel beam, with A_w the area of the web, A_t the area of the top flange, and A_b the area of the bottom flange:

$$\frac{S_{bs}}{(A_w + 2A_b)d_w} = \frac{S_{ts}}{(A_w + 2A_t)d_w} \approx \frac{1}{2}\left(\frac{\frac{1}{6} + \frac{A_t}{A_w}}{1 + 2\frac{A_t}{A_w}} + \frac{\frac{1}{6} + \frac{A_b}{A_w}}{1 + 2\frac{A_b}{A_w}} \right)$$

(2-10a)

Observing further that the term $\frac{1}{12}A_c t^2$ in Eq. (2-3f) is negligible, the following approximate expressions may be obtained from Eqs. (2-3) for the bottom- and top-flange section moduli of the composite beam:

$$\frac{S_{bc}}{(A_w + 2A_b)d_w} \approx \frac{\left(\frac{1}{2}K_b + \frac{e_c}{d_w}\right)^2 \frac{K_c}{K_b} + \frac{S_{bs}}{2(A_w + 2A_b)d_w}K_t}{\frac{1}{2}K_t + \left(\frac{1}{2}K_b + \frac{e_c}{d_w}\right)K_c}$$

(2-10b)

$$\frac{S_{tc}}{(A_w + 2A_t)d_w} \approx \frac{\left(\frac{1}{2}K_b + \frac{e_c}{d_w}\right)^2 \frac{K_c}{K_t} + \frac{S_{ts}}{2(A_w + 2A_t)d_w}K_b}{\frac{1}{2}K_b - \left(\frac{1}{2}K_b + \frac{e_c}{d_w}\right)K_c} \qquad (2\text{-}10c)$$

where

$$K_b = \frac{1 + 2(A_b/A_w)}{1 + (A_b/A_w) + (A_t/A_w)}$$

$$K_t = \frac{1 + 2(A_t/A_w)}{1 + (A_b/A_w) + (A_t/A_w)}$$

$$K_c = \frac{A_c}{A_c + A_s}$$

It may be noted that the right-hand sides of Eqs. (2-10) may be evaluated if K_c, e_c/d_w, and the ratios A_b/A_w and A_t/A_w are known approximately. A graphical solution of Eq. (2-10a) is given in Fig. 5-3, and graphical solutions of Eqs. (2-10b) and (2-10c) are given in Figs. 5-4 to 5-15 for several combinations of A_b/A_w and A_t/A_w covering the practical ranges of values. The number of combinations is sufficient so that no interpolation is necessary. Figures 5-4 to 5-15 include several values of e_c/d_w covering the practical range; for intermediate values of e_c/d_w straight-line interpolation gives satisfactory results.

Figures 5-3 to 5-15 (or the corresponding equations) may be used in selection of the cross section as is shown in the remainder of this article.[1]

The maximum allowable stress governs the size of the bottom and top flanges. By procedures similar to that described for rolled beams in Arts. 2-11 and 2-12, the following expressions may be obtained from the stress equations:

$$A_w + 2A_b = \frac{M_{Ds}}{f_b}\frac{(A_w + 2A_b)d_w}{S_{bs}}\frac{1}{d_w} + \frac{M_{Dc}}{f_b}\frac{(A_w + 2A_b)d_w}{S_{bc}}\frac{1}{d_w}$$
$$+ \frac{M_{LL}}{f_b}\frac{(A_w + 2A_b)d_w}{S_{bc}}\frac{1}{d_w} \qquad (2\text{-}11a)$$

$$A_w + 2A_t = \frac{M_{Ds}}{f_b}\frac{(A_w + 2A_t)d_w}{S_{ts}}\frac{1}{d_w} + \frac{M_{Dc}}{f_b}\frac{(A_w + 2A_t)d_w}{S_{tc}}\frac{1}{d_w}$$
$$+ \frac{M_{LL}}{f_t}\frac{(A_w + 2A_t)d_w}{S_{tc}}\frac{1}{d_w} \qquad (2\text{-}11b)$$

[1] Equations (2-10) are applicable to any unsymmetrical section and, therefore, also to rolled beams with a cover plate. A comparison of Eqs. (2-10) with Eqs. (2-6) reveals that the effect of the addition of a cover plate is small. Thus a rolled beam with a cover plate may be selected for a composite beam with the aid of Figs. 5-1 and 5-2 as described in Art. 2-12.

The necessary areas for the bottom and top flanges may be computed from Eqs. (2-11a) and (2-11b) using the appropriate graphs in Figs. 5-3 to 5-15 for the assumed area ratios.

If the depth of the web is assumed first, the thickness may be computed from the AASHO limitation in Art. 1.6.75 (for carbon steel, $t_w \geq d_w/170$); the assumed web area is then $t_w d_w$. The ratios A_t/A_w and A_b/A_w for plate girders usually fall in the range of Figs. 5-10 and 5-11. Figure 5-10 applies to spans greater than about 80 ft, while Fig. 5-11 applies to shorter spans.

The procedure for selecting the size of a plate girder is illustrated in Example 2-3. The ratios A_t/A_w and A_b/A_w are purposely estimated low for the first trial in order to illustrate the procedure for correcting poor estimates of such ratios.

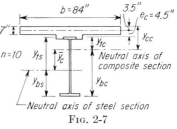

Fig. 2-7

Example 2-3. Design an unshored welded plate girder for the composite beam shown in Fig. 2-7. Allowable stresses are $f_c = 1,200$ psi and $f_t = f_b = 18,000$ psi. Moments are as follows:

$$M_{Ds} = 2,700 \text{ kip-ft}$$
$$M_{Dc} = 1,800 \text{ kip-ft}$$
$$M_{LL} = 2,700 \text{ kip-ft}$$

Determine for each moment the required section modulus for a noncomposite beam (as for Examples 2-1 and 2-2). Thus,

$$S_s = 2,700 \times \frac{12 \times 1,000}{18,000} = 1,800 \text{ in.}^3$$

$$S_s = 1,800 \times \frac{12 \times 1,000}{18,000} = 1,200 \text{ in.}^3$$

$$S_s = 1,800 \text{ in.}^3$$

Assume that $d_w = 96$ in., $A_t/A_w = 0.3$, $A_b/A_w = 0.5$, $t_w = \frac{5}{8}$ in., $A_w = 60$ in.², $A_s = 60(1 + 0.3 + 0.5) = 108$ in.².

With the known value of e_c and the assumed value of d_w,

$$\frac{e_c}{d_w} = \frac{4.5}{96} = 0.0469$$

With the assumed values of A_t/A_w and A_b/A_w, Fig. 5-3 gives

$$\frac{S_{bs}}{A_w + 2A_b} = \frac{S_{ts}}{A_w + 2A_t} = 0.312 \times 96 = 29.95 \text{ in.}$$

When $k = 3$ for determining the transformed concrete area,

$$A_c = \frac{bt}{kn} = \frac{84 \times 7}{3 \times 10} = 19.6 \text{ in.}^2$$

and

$$K_c = \frac{A_c}{A_c + A_s} = \frac{19.6}{19.6 + 108} = 0.1536$$

Then from Fig. 5-9,

$$\frac{S_{bc}}{(A_w + 2A_b)d_w} = 0.352$$

and

$$\frac{(A_w + 2A_t)d_w}{S_{tc}} = 1.96$$

When $k = 1$ for determining the transformed concrete area,

$$A_c = \frac{84 \times 7}{1 \times 10} = 58.8 \text{ in.}^2$$

and

$$K_c = \frac{58.8}{58.8 \times 108} = 0.3525$$

Then from Fig. 5-9,

$$\frac{S_{bc}}{(A_w + 2A_b)d_w} = 0.387$$

$$\frac{(A_w + 2A_t)d_w}{S_{tc}} = 1.11$$

First Trial Section [substituting in Eqs. (2-11)]

Top flange:

$$A_{Ds} = \frac{1,800}{29.95} = 60.1 \text{ in.}^2$$

$$A_{Dc} = \frac{1,200 \times 1.96}{96} = 24.5$$

$$A_{LL} = \frac{1,800 \times 1.11}{96} = 20.8$$

$$A_w + 2A_t = 105.4 \text{ in.}^2$$

$$A_w = 60.0$$

$$2A_t = 45.4 \text{ in.}^2$$

$$A_t = \frac{45.4}{2} = 22.7 \text{ in.}^2$$

Bottom flange:

$$A_{Ds} = \frac{1,800}{29.95} = 60.1 \text{ in.}^2$$

$$A_{Dc} = \frac{1,200}{0.352 \times 96} = 35.5$$

$$A_{LL} = \frac{1,800}{0.387 \times 96} = 48.5$$

$$A_w + 2A_b = 144.1 \text{ in.}^2$$

$$A_w = 60.0$$

$$2A_b = 84.1 \text{ in.}^2$$

$$A_b = \frac{84.1}{2} = 42.0 \text{ in.}^2$$

Adding the computed required areas A_t and A_b to the assumed web area A_w gives the total required steel area:

$$A_s = 22.7 + 42 + 60 = 124.7 \text{ in.}^2$$

This is considerably higher than the estimated A_s of 108 in.². It will be necessary, therefore, to run through another trial. New values for the ratios of flange steel to web steel can be determined from the computed values for A_t and A_b. Thus,

$$\frac{A_t}{A_w} = \frac{22.7}{60} = 0.378$$

and

$$\frac{A_b}{A_w} = \frac{42}{60} = 0.70$$

Then, from Fig. 5-3, as in the first trial,

$$\frac{S_{bs}}{A_w + 2A_b} = \frac{S_{ts}}{A_w + 2A_t} = 0.334 \times 96 = 32.1$$

When $k = 3$, the revised $K_c = 19.6/(19.6 + 124.7) = 0.1356$, and from Fig. 5-10, plotted for A_t/A_w and A_b/A_w values closer to the new values for those ratios,

$$\frac{S_{bc}}{(A_w + 2A_b)d_w} = 0.371$$

and

$$\frac{(A_w + 2A_t)d_w}{S_{tc}} = 1.87$$

When $k = 1$, $K_c = 58.8/(58.8 + 124.7) = 0.32$ and from Fig. 5-10

$$\frac{S_{bc}}{(A_w + 2A_b)d_w} = 0.403$$

and

$$\frac{(A_w + 2A_t)d_w}{S_{tc}} = 1.06$$

Second Trial Section [again applying Eqs. (2-11)]

Top flange:

$$A_{Ds} = \frac{1,800}{32} \qquad = 56.1 \text{ in.}^2$$

$$A_{Dc} = \frac{1,200 \times 1.87}{96} = 23.4$$

$$A_{LL} = \frac{1,800 \times 1.06}{96} = 19.9$$

$$A_w + 2A_t = \overline{99.4 \text{ in.}^2}$$
$$A_w = 60.0$$
$$2A_t = \overline{39.4 \text{ in.}^2}$$

$$A_t = \frac{39.4}{2} = 19.7 \text{ in.}^2$$

Try 16- by 1¼-in. top plate = 20.0 in.².
Bottom flange:

$$A_{Ds} = \frac{1,800}{32} \qquad = 56.1 \text{ in.}^2$$

$$A_{Dc} = \frac{1,200}{0.371 \times 96} = 33.7$$

$$A_{LL} = \frac{1,800}{0.403 \times 96} = 46.5$$

$$A_w + 2A_b = \overline{136.3 \text{ in.}^2}$$
$$A_w = 60.0$$
$$2A_b = \overline{76.3 \text{ in.}^2}$$

$$A_b = \frac{76.3}{2} = 38.2 \text{ in.}^2$$

Try 24- by 1⅝-in. bottom plate = 39.0 in.².

Adding the computed flange areas and the assumed web area gives the total required area. Thus,

$$A_s = 20 + 39 + 60 = 119 \text{ in.}^2$$

This area is within the assumed area of 124.7 in.², with which the second trial was begun. Therefore, the second trial section is suitable.

Properties of Second Trial Section

Steel section [from Eqs. (2-2)]:

$$\bar{y}_s = \frac{\frac{1}{2}(d_w + t_b)A_b - \frac{1}{2}(d_w + t_t)A_t}{A_s}$$

$$= \frac{(96 + 1.63)39 - (96 + 1.25)20}{2 \times 119} = 7.83 \text{ in.}$$

$$\begin{aligned}
I_s &= \frac{1}{4}(d_w + t_t)^2 A_t + \frac{1}{4}(d_w + t_b)^2 A_b + I_w - A_s \bar{y}_s^2 \\
&= \frac{1}{4}(97.63^2 \times 39 + 97.25^2 \times 20) \\
&\quad + \frac{1}{12} \times 96^3 \times 0.63 - 119 \times 7.83^2 = 179,400 \text{ in.}^4
\end{aligned}$$

$$y_{ts} = \frac{1}{2}d_w + t_t + \bar{y}_s = 48 + 1.25 + 7.83 = 57.1 \text{ in.}$$

$$S_{ts} = \frac{I_s}{y_{ts}} = 3,140 \text{ in.}^3$$

$$y_{bs} = \frac{1}{2}d_w + t_b - \bar{y}_s = 48 + 1.63 - 7.83 = 41.8 \text{ in.}$$

$$S_{bs} = \frac{I_s}{y_{bs}} = 4,290 \text{ in.}^3$$

Composite section [from Eqs. (2-3)] with $k = 3$:

$$K_c = \frac{A_c}{A_c + A_s} = \frac{19.6}{19.6 + 119} = 0.1414$$

$$\bar{y}_c = (y_{ts} + e_c)K_c = (57.08 + 4.5)0.1414 = 8.71 \text{ in.}$$

$$\begin{aligned}
I_c &= (y_{ts} + e_c)\bar{y}_c A_s + I_s + A_c \frac{t^2}{12} = 8.71 \times 61.58 \times 119 \\
&\quad + 179,400 + \frac{19.6 \times 7^2}{12} = 243,300 \text{ in.}^4
\end{aligned}$$

$$y_{tc} = y_{ts} - \bar{y}_c = 57.08 - 8.71 = 48.37 \text{ in.}$$

$$S_{tc} = \frac{I_c}{y_{tc}} = 5,030 \text{ in.}^3$$

$$y_{bc} = y_{bs} + \bar{y}_c = 41.8 + 8.71 = 50.51 \text{ in.}$$

$$S_{bc} = \frac{I_c}{y_{bc}} = 4,820 \text{ in.}^3$$

$$y_{cc} = y_{tc} + e_c + \frac{t}{2} = 48.4 + 4.5 + 3.5 = 56.4 \text{ in.}$$

$$S_{cc} = \frac{I_c}{y_{cc}} = 4,315 \text{ in.}^3$$

Composite section with $k = 1$:

$$K_c = \frac{58.8}{58.8 + 119} = 0.331$$

$\bar{y}_c = 61.58 \times 0.331 = 20.4$ in.

$I_c = 20.4 \times 61.58 \times 119 + 179,400 + \dfrac{58.8 \times 7^2}{12}$

$\qquad = 328,800$ in.^{4}

$y_{tc} = 57.1 - 20.4 = 36.7$ in.

$S_{tc} = 8,950$ in.^{3}

$y_{bc} = 41.8 + 20.4 = 62.2$ in.

$S_{bc} = 5,290$ in.^{3}

$y_{cc} = 36.7 + 4.5 + 3.5 = 44.7$ in.

$S_{cc} = 7,350$ in.^{3}

Stresses

	f_c, ksi	f_t, ksi	f_b, ksi
DLs	0	$\dfrac{2,700 \times 12}{3,140} = 10.31$	$\dfrac{32,400}{4,290} = 7.56$
DLc	$\dfrac{1,800 \times 12}{4,315 \times 30} = 0.17$	$\dfrac{21,600}{5,030} = 4.29$	$\dfrac{21,600}{4,820} = 4.48$
LL	$\dfrac{2,700 \times 12}{7,350 \times 10} = 0.44$	$\dfrac{32,400}{8,950} = 3.62$	$\dfrac{32,400}{5,290} = 6.12$
	$\overline{0.61}$	$\overline{18.22}$	$\overline{18.16}$

2-14. Length of Cover Plate

In a composite T beam with the steel section made up of a symmetrical rolled section and a steel cover plate, the cover plate may be cut off short of the supports. The computation of the theoretical length of the cover plate is based on the same principles used in the design of steel sections.

If a portion of the total load is carried by the steel beam alone, an exact computation of the theoretical length is very tedious. However, an approximate calculation can be made on the assumption that the bottom-flange stress caused by the noncomposite dead load at the end of the cover plate is equal to the bottom-flange stress caused by the same dead load at the section of maximum moment.

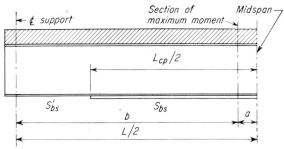

FIG. 2-8. Length of cover plate.

Using the notation of Fig. 2-8 and designating the moment due to noncomposite dead load at the end of the cover plate as M'_{Ds} and the corresponding bottom-flange section modulus as S'_{bs}, it is assumed that

$$\frac{M'_{Ds}}{S'_{bs}} = \frac{M_{Ds}}{S_{bs}}$$

The dead-load moment has a parabolic distribution; therefore,

$$M'_{Ds} = M_{Ds} \left\{ 1 - \left[\frac{(L_{cp}/2) - a}{b} \right]^2 \right\} \qquad (2\text{-}12a)$$

But $b = L/2 - a$; so the theoretical length of the cover plate L_{cp} may be expressed as follows:

$$L_{cp} = (L - 2a) \sqrt{1 - \frac{S'_{bs}}{S_{bs}}} + 2a \qquad (2\text{-}12b)$$

where L_{cp} = theoretical length of cover plate

L = span length

a = distance of maximum-moment section from midspan

S'_{bs} = section modulus for bottom flange of rolled beam alone

S_{bs} = section modulus for bottom flange of steel beam including cover plate

In beams with temporary supports all dead load is carried by the composite section. The approximate length of the cover plate may be computed on the basis of the composite dead load from the following formula:

$$L_{cp} = (L - 2a) \sqrt{1 - \frac{S'_{bc}}{S_{bc}}} + 2a \qquad (2\text{-}12c)$$

where S'_{bc} = section modulus for bottom flange of composite
beam without cover plate computed with $k = 3$

S_{bc} = section modulus for bottom flange of composite
beam with cover plate computed with $k = 3$

Equations (2-12) are based on full allowable stress at the theoretical cutoff point of the cover plate. The actual length of the plate should extend at least 1 ft beyond the theoretical points of cutoff.

It should be noted that the equation for L_{cp} gives only an approximate theoretical length of the cover plate. It is necessary, therefore, to check the actual stress at the theoretical cutoff point after its position has been determined. The total bottom-flange stress, including the noncomposite dead load, the composite dead load, and the live load, must not exceed the allowable value.

2-15. Continuous Beams

Continuous spans, of either composite or noncomposite construction, are often advantageous when foundation conditions and desired span lengths are favorable for this type of construction. When foundations do not permit continuous structures, cantilever spans can be used; they yield similar benefits.

The principal advantages of continuous spans as compared with simple spans are materials savings in main carrying members and possible corresponding dollar savings, increased span lengths, and shallower construction when clearances are a design factor. These advantages are further enhanced when composite continuous construction is used.

In addition, composite construction increases the stiffness and the ultimate carrying capacities. The increase of stiffness leads to a decrease in live-load deflections and vibrations; the increase of the ultimate capacity results in an increased factor of safety.

In continuous composite beams, as in simple composite beams, the noncomposite dead loads are carried by the steel section alone while the composite dead loads are carried by the steel section plus the portion of the slab acting compositely. The effectiveness of the slab in resisting the composite dead loads is affected by creep; therefore the corresponding calculations are usually based on $kn = 3E_s/E_c$. The live loads are also carried by the steel section plus the portion of the slab acting compositely;

Continuous welded plate girder bridge at Ft. Pierre, S. Dak., was designed for composite action in regions of positive bending moment.

Studs to transmit shear were welded to the top flange of the continuous girders only where positive moment occurs.

however, the effectiveness of the slab is not affected by creep, so that $kn = E_s/E_c$ should be used.

It can be seen readily from the elastic theory that the changes in resisting sections from one type of loading condition to another will produce corresponding changes in the distribution of moments. Thus, it is necessary to calculate the physical properties for two different beam sections when shored construction is used and three different beam sections when unshored construction is used.

Concrete is generally assumed ineffective in resisting tension and thus cannnot be counted on to resist negative moments in the continuous beam. This restricts the use of the concrete slab as a cover plate (composite section) to the predominantly positive-moment regions between the dead-load points of inflection. Other factors may determine the exact length of the composite section. One of the more important of these is the desired position of field splices, which often depend on construction requirements and on the location of lateral bracing connections to the main girders. Special care should be exercised if the slab is made composite over riveted or bolted splices. Shear connectors must be spaced so as to avoid flange rivets or bolts, because the heat generated by welding of the connectors may have an adverse effect on high-tensile bolts or rivets if sufficient clearance is not provided. If welded splices are used, the shear connectors do not interfere and have no damaging effect. Some designers prefer composite slabs with no construction joints. Practical pour lengths may then restrict the length of the composite section.

2-16. Negative-moment Sections in Continuous Beams

The concrete in the negative-moment regions can transfer shear to longitudinal reinforcing steel which may be placed in the slab as an aid in resisting the negative moments. If steel is placed in the slab for this purpose, the shear connectors must be used throughout the beam length for proper shear transfer. If this steel is not used, then the shear connectors need not be placed in the negative-moment regions and should extend only through the length of the slab acting as a cover plate.

The placing of additional longitudinal steel in the slab may not increase the section sufficiently to resist the negative-moment stresses in the bottom flange. The additional required increase in section may be provided for by adding a small cover plate on the top flange and a larger cover plate on the bottom flange if rolled beams are used or by increasing the flange sizes as necessary if built-up girders are used.

It should be noted that the longitudinal steel does not share in resisting noncomposite dead loads. Thus the most efficient method of providing for negative moments is to increase the main steel section only. This is done by a symmetrical increase in both flanges by the addition of equal cover plates or equal increases in both flange plates.

If the design is based on the assumption that the negative moments are carried solely by the steel section, a symmetrical steel section is desired. Observing that for a symmetrical section $\bar{y}_s = 0$, the necessary area of each cover plate for a rolled beam can be evaluated from the following formula:

$$A_p = \frac{(M/f_a)(d + 2t_p) - 2I_B}{(d + t_p)^2} \qquad (2\text{-}13a)$$

where M = maximum negative moment
f_a = allowable steel stress
d = depth of rolled beam
t_p = assumed thickness of cover plate
I_B = moment of inertia of rolled beam

The flange areas for a symmetrical built-up girder can be evaluated from the following formula:

$$A_t = A_b = \frac{M}{f_a d_w} - \frac{A_w}{6} \qquad (2\text{-}13b)$$

where d_w = depth of web
A_w = area of web

2-17. Distribution of Moments in Continuous Beams

The distribution of moments in a continuous beam is related to the ratio of the moment of inertia of the maximum-positive-moment section to the moment of inertia of the negative-moment section. The smaller this ratio, the larger is the negative moment. When the distribution of moments in a composite beam is compared with the distribution in a noncomposite beam, the following relationships should be noted:

1. The ratio of the moment of inertia of the maximum-negative-moment section to the moment of inertia of the steel section at the location of the maximum positive moment in a composite beam is greater than the corresponding ratio in a noncomposite beam. This relationship is important in connection with the moments caused by noncomposite dead loads.

2. The ratio of the moment of inertia of the maximum-negative-moment section to the moment of inertia of the composite section for $k = 3$ at the location of the maximum positive moment in a composite beam is about the same as the corresponding ratio in a noncomposite beam. This relationship is important in considering the moments caused by composite dead loads.

3. The ratio of the moment of inertia of the maximum-negative-moment section to the moment of inertia of the composite section for $k = 1$ at the location of the maximum positive moment in a composite beam is smaller than the corresponding ratio in a noncomposite beam. This relationship is important in considering the moments caused by live loads.

Accordingly, the noncomposite dead loads cause larger negative moments in a composite beam than in a noncomposite beam, the composite dead loads cause about the same negative moments in both cases, and the live loads cause smaller negative moments in the composite beam.

Preliminary designs for continuous composite spans with rolled sections can be made quite accurately, with slight adjustments in the allowable stresses, from influence lines for prismatic members. The relatively large moments of inertia in the positive-moment regions for live loads tend to compensate for the relatively large moments of inertia in the negative-moment regions for noncomposite dead loads. This compensation, plus a decrease in the allowable stress of about 3 per cent for negative moments and an increase in the allowable stress for positive moment of about 4 per cent, should yield a preliminary design very close to the final design sections.

Preliminary designs for continuous composite spans with variable-depth plate girders made from influence lines for continuous noncomposite variable-depth girders of the same geometric shape yield, in most cases, accurate results without any adjustments of the allowable stresses.

Separate moment and shear curves should be constructed for

each type of loading condition acting on the continuous unit. Complete maximum-positive- and maximum-negative-moment curves indicate the possible necessity of considering reversal of stress in the beam at or near the inflection points. Occasionally this reversal of stress will dictate the size of rolled section or minimum plate-girder section for the positive-moment regions. Cover-plate cutoffs are also determined from the moment curves. Separate shear curves are necessary to determine the spacing of shear connectors.

2-18. Deflections

Deflections of composite beams are calculated by the same analytical methods as are used for other types of beams. The methods of least work, moment areas, elastic weights, and others give reasonably accurate results if proper values of the modular ratio are chosen.

Composite beams are frequently nonprismatic, so that exact computations of deflections would have to account for the changes in the moment of inertia. However, it is sufficiently accurate in many cases to base the deflection computations on the moment of inertia of the maximum-positive-moment section and to neglect the section variations along the beam. The error caused by this approximation is particularly small for simple beams with variable size of the bottom flanges. It is usually of the order of 1 per cent and is almost always less than 3 per cent.

The formulas presented in the following articles were derived for prismatic beams. The designer will find it expedient to use these formulas for all types of beams, especially in computing the live-load deflections. However, if the calculations give deflections close to the allowable maximum, it may be desirable to check the results by a more accurate method.

2-19. Dead-load Deflections

A composite beam usually is subjected to both composite and noncomposite dead loads. Thus, in calculating the dead-load deflections, it is necessary to consider two beam sections. The deflections caused by noncomposite dead loads are computed with the properties of the steel beam alone, and the deflections caused by composite dead loads are computed with the properties of the composite section.   The total deflection is then equal to the sum of the two separate deflections.

Composite dead loads cause stresses in the slab.   These stresses lead to creep of concrete and to an increase of deflections with time.   The increase of deflections caused by creep of concrete may be accounted for in the design by increasing the modular ratio.   Although in computing the immediate deflections (not including the effects of creep) a value of $kn = E_s/E_c$ gives reasonably accurate results, the final deflections agree better with values based on $kn = 3E_s/E_c$.

Unless effective temporary supports are used during the construction, the dead-load deflections are affected by the sequence of concreting the slab.   The first section placed sets and becomes at least partly composite before the next pour is made. However, observations of deflections during construction of several bridges have indicated that if pours are made within reasonably short time intervals, creep of concrete reduces this partial composite effect to a negligible amount. Hence, the effect of the sequence of pouring is usually disregarded in deflection computations.

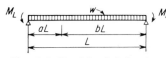

FIG. 2-9. Dead-load deflection.

With the notation shown in Fig. 2-9, the dead-load deflection at any point on the beam can be computed from the following formula:

$$\Delta_{aL} = \frac{72wL^4}{E_s I}\, ab[1 + ab - 4(C_R - C_L)(1 + a) - 12C_L] \quad (2\text{-}14a)$$

where Δ_{aL} = deflection at distance aL from left support, in.

w = dead load, kips per ft

L = span length, ft

E_s = modulus of elasticity of steel, ksi

I = moment of inertia of steel section or of composite section, in.[4]

$C_R = M_R/wL^2$

$C_L = M_L/wL^2$

M_R, M_L = restraining moments at right and left supports, respectively, kip-ft

In a simply supported beam $M_R = M_L = 0$, so that the deflection formula is reduced to the following form:

$$\Delta_{aL} = \frac{72wL^4}{E_s I} ab(1 + ab) \qquad (2\text{-}14b)$$

The maximum dead-load deflection of a simply supported beam occurs at mid-span:

$$\Delta = \frac{45wL^4}{2E_s I} \qquad (2\text{-}14c)$$

2-20. Live-load Deflections

Live loads are resisted by the composite section. Since live loads are of short duration, the live-load deflections should be computed with section properties based on $kn = E_s/E_c$. The deflection caused by live load including impact should not exceed $\frac{1}{800}$ of the span, the span length being considered the distance center to center of bearings. Live-load deflections rarely control the design of composite beams unless shored construction is used.

The following formulas for simple spans and for intermediate spans of continuous beams give live-load deflections at mid-span with the loads placed for the maximum simple-span positive moment. The formulas for the end spans of continuous beams give live-load deflections at the distance of $0.4L$ from the simple support with the loads placed for the maximum simple-span moment at the same section. Although such deflections are not necessarily the largest which may occur in the span, they are close to the maximum values.

The following formulas apply to simple beams and to intermediate spans of continuous beams:

H-S trucks:

$$\Delta = \frac{324}{E_s I_c} \left[P_T(L^3 - 555L + 4{,}780) - \frac{1}{3}(M_R + M_L)L^2 \right] \qquad (2\text{-}15a)$$

H trucks:

$$\Delta = \frac{180}{E_s I_c} [P_T(L^3 - 200L + 1{,}610) - 0.6(M_R + M_L)L^2] \qquad (2\text{-}15b)$$

Lane loads:

$$\Delta = \frac{45L^2}{2E_s I_c} [L(w_L L + 1.6P_L) - 4.8(M_R + M_L)] \qquad (2\text{-}15c)$$

where Δ = center-line deflection, in.

P_T = weight of one front truck wheel, kips, multiplied by live-load distribution factor plus impact

I_c = moment of inertia of composite section based on $kn = E_s/E_c$, in.[4]

w_L = one-half weight of uniform lane load, kips per ft, multiplied by distribution factor plus impact

P_L = one-half weight of concentrated lane load for moment, kips, multiplied by distribution factor plus impact

For simple beams $M_R = M_L = 0$.

The following formulas apply to the end spans of continuous beams:

H-S trucks:

$$\Delta_{0.4} = \frac{300}{E_s I_c} [P_T(L^3 + 3.89L^2 - 680L + 5{,}910) - 0.32ML^2]$$

$$(2\text{-}16a)$$

H trucks:

$$\Delta_{0.4} = \frac{166}{E_s I_c} [P_T(L^3 + 2.33L^2 - 245L + 1{,}910) - 0.58ML^2]$$

$$(2\text{-}16b)$$

Lane loads:

$$\Delta_{0.4} = \frac{43L^2}{2E_s I_c} [L(w_L L + 1.5P_L) - 4.5M] \qquad (2\text{-}16c)$$

where $\Delta_{0.4}$ = deflection at distance of $0.4L$ from simple support, in.

M = restraining moment at continuous support, kip-ft

2-21. Slenderness Limitations

The AASHO specifications, Art. 1.9.6, suggest two limiting slenderness ratios for composite beams. The slenderness limitations are aimed at preventing excessive vibrations. Although they do not account for several important factors known to influence the vibrations of bridges, the slenderness limitations and the limiting live-load deflections are the only readily usable measures against excessive vibrations.

It is suggested that the over-all depth of the composite section, i.e., the depth from the top face of the slab to the bottom face of the steel beam or girder, be at least $\frac{1}{25}$ of the span. Furthermore, the depth of the steel section should not be less than $\frac{1}{30}$ of the span. The span is the distance center to center of bearings for simple beams and the distance between the dead-load points of contraflexure for continuous beams. If depths less than these are used, the sections should be so increased that the maximum deflection is not greater than if these ratios had not been exceeded.

CHAPTER 3

SHEAR CONNECTORS

3-1. Design Assumptions

The concrete slab and the steel beams in composite construction form one structural unit. They are interconnected with shear connectors capable of (1) transferring horizontal shear and (2) resisting relative movements between the slab and the beams. The shear connectors must be capable of resisting both horizontal and vertical movements.

Bond between the slab concrete and the flanges of the steel beams may provide some degree of composite action. However, bond may be broken during the life of the structure and, therefore, should not be relied on for the transfer of shear. It must be assumed in the design computations, therefore, that all shears caused by forces acting on the composite structure are transmitted by the shear connectors.

3-2. Loading Conditions

Live loads, impact, dead loads applied after the concrete has attained sufficient strength to resist the horizontal shear, removal of shoring, creep, and shrinkage of concrete constitute the forces and force-producing effects to be considered.

For bridges, the *live load* is usually of short duration and always acting on the composite section. Thus the shear connectors must be designed for full live load including the effect of impact. As a moving load, the live load may cause reversal of stresses in a shear connector.

Dead load may be carried either by the steel beams alone or by the composite section. Shear connectors should be designed only for the portion of dead load carried by the composite section. It may be assumed in the design that all dead loads applied after the concrete has attained 75 per cent of its 28-day strength are carried by the composite section. Furthermore, for beams built with three or more fully effective temporary supports between the ends, it is sufficiently accurate to assume that all dead loads are carried by the composite section. If fewer temporary supports are used for shoring, however, it is necessary to consider in the design the actual shear caused by shore removal.

Dead loads and the removal of shores cause permanent stresses leading to creep (plastic flow) of concrete. The effect of creep is to relieve stresses in the concrete slab and thus to decrease the

Ready for placing of concrete floor slab, steel forms span between floor beams, which are studded with welded shear connectors for composite action, in the International Business Machine photographic laboratory, Poughkeepsie, New York.

forces transmitted by the shear connectors. Creep is a time-dependent phenomenon; it progresses several months before the stress relief that it causes is fully materialized. Therefore, the effects of creep should be disregarded in the design of shear connectors.

During the first few months after construction, the concrete slab shrinks; the *shrinkage* is resisted by the shear connectors. In simple beams and in the positive-moment regions of continuous beams the shrinkage loads on shear connectors act in a direction opposite the direction of maximum horizontal shear caused by the dead and live load. In the negative-moment regions of continuous beams the concrete slab is stressed in tension and, in the design, considered ineffective. Thus a possible overstress of shear connectors in the negative-moment region is relatively unimportant. Effects of shrinkage may, therefore, be disregarded in the design of shear connectors.

Expansion of concrete and differential temperature changes are examples of other effects which have to be considered in exceptional cases. However, *ordinarily it is desirable and safe to design shear connectors only for the forces caused by the dead load carried by the composite section and the live load including impact.*

3-3. Horizontal Shear

The horizontal shear between the concrete slab and the steel beam is given by the following formula:

$$S = \frac{V_c m}{I_c} \tag{3-1}$$

where S = horizontal shear of steel flange at the junction of the slab and beam, lb per lin in.

V_c = vertical shear, acting on the composite section, lb

m = statical moment of the transformed concrete area about the neutral axis of the composite section (using $kn = E_s/E_c$) or the statical moment of the area of reinforcement embedded in the slab for negative moment, in.[3]

I_c = moment of inertia of the transformed composite section (using $kn = E_s/E_c$), in.[4]

The m/I_c values for some common sections are listed in Table 5-3. Others may be computed from formulas (2-3) in Art. 2-7.

3-4. Design Load for One Shear Connector

At working load, the resistance value of one shear connector is its useful capacity divided by the factor of safety:

$$Q = \frac{Q_{uc}}{\text{FS}} \tag{3-2}$$

Useful capacity Q_{uc} of a shear connector is the load beyond which the shear connector permits an appreciable slip between the concrete slab and the steel beam. The magnitude of the useful capacity of various shear connectors was established experimentally; the resulting equations are given in this article.

One principle in structural design is to design equal strength into all components of a structure. This structure, having no weak point, will carry the greatest load at a minimum cost. For composite construction, this principle requires shear connectors equal in strength to the beam and the slab acting compositely. An equation [Eq. (3-6)] for the factor of safety based on this principle is given in Art. 3-5.

Tests of granular-flux-filled welded studs have shown that the useful capacity of one stud can be computed from the following formulas:

for $h_s/d_s \geqq 4.2$

$$Q_{uc} = 330d_s{}^2 \sqrt{f_c'} \qquad (3\text{-}3a)$$

for $h_s/d_s < 4.2$

$$Q_{uc} = 80h_s d_s \sqrt{f_c'} \qquad (3\text{-}3b)$$

where Q_{uc} = useful capacity of one stud, lb

d_s = stud diameter, in.

h_s = stud height, in.

f_c' = 28-day compressive strength of 6- by 12-in. concrete cylinders, psi

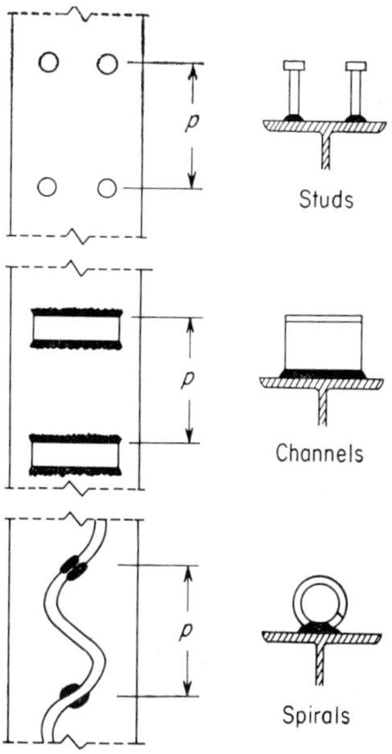

The most commonly used stud diameters are $\tfrac{5}{8}$, $\tfrac{3}{4}$, and $\tfrac{7}{8}$ in. Their useful capacities are given in Table 5-4a for various values of f_c'.

Fig. 3-1. Types of shear connectors.

The useful capacity of a flexible-channel shear connector made of structural-grade steel is given by the formula

$$Q_{uc} = 180(h + 0.5t)w \sqrt{f_c'} \qquad (3\text{-}4)$$

and the useful capacity of one turn of spiral shear connector is given by the formula

$$Q_{uc} = 3{,}840d_{sp} \sqrt[4]{f_c'} \qquad (3\text{-}5)$$

where h = maximum thickness of channel flange, in. (Table 5-4b)

t = thickness of channel web, in. (Table 5-4b)

w = width of channel connector, in.

d_{sp} = diameter of the spiral bar, in.

f'_c = 28-day compressive strength of 6- by 12-in. concrete cylinders, psi

3-5. Factor of Safety (FS)

In general, a portion of the dead load is carried by the steel beam alone. The remaining dead load and the live load are carried by the composite section. If the structure is overloaded, the dead load remains unchanged but the live load is increased. Accordingly, a factor of safety assuring shear connectors equal in strength to the composite beam depends on (1) the ratio of the strength of the unaided steel section to the strength of the composite section and (2) the ratio of the dead load to the live load. The following factor-of-safety equation, based upon the principle of equal strength, is recommended for the design of shear connectors:

$$\text{FS} = \frac{A(1 + C_{mc} + C_{mi}C_s) - (C_{mc} + C_{mi}) + C_v}{1 + C_v} \quad (3\text{-}6)$$

where $C_{mc} = \dfrac{\text{max moment caused by DL}}{\text{max moment caused by LL}} = \dfrac{M_{Dc}}{M_{LL}}$
$\qquad\qquad\quad\text{acting on composite section}$

$\quad C_{mi} = \dfrac{\text{max moment caused by DL}}{\text{max moment caused by LL}} = \dfrac{M_{Ds}}{M_{LL}}$
$\qquad\qquad\quad\text{acting on steel beam alone}$

$\quad C_s = \dfrac{\text{section modulus of composite beam for extreme tension fibers}}{\text{section modulus of steel beam for extreme tension fibers}} = \dfrac{S_{bc}}{S_{bs}}$

$\quad C_v = \dfrac{\text{vertical shear caused by DL}}{\text{vertical shear caused by LL}} = \dfrac{V_{Dc}}{V_{LL}}$
$\qquad\qquad\quad\text{acting on composite section}$

$\quad A$ = numerical factor depending on properties of composite beam and on design requirements

If it is required to retain composite action up to first yielding of the steel beam, the numerical constant $A = 1.8$ gives a satisfactory design for beams of structural-grade steel proportioned for $f_s = 18{,}000$ psi. On the other hand, if it is required to retain composite action at all levels of loading, $A = 2.7$ gives a satisfactory design for beams of structural-grade steel proportioned for $f_s = 18{,}000$ psi. The higher of the two factors is preferable, since it guarantees all advantages of composite action at the relatively low cost of a few additional shear connectors. Factor $A = 2.7$ is required by the AASHO specifications, Art. 1.9.5.

The term $A(1 + C_{mc} + C_{mi}C_s) - (C_{mc} + C_{mi})$ in Eq. (3-6) is equal to the design live-load multiple corresponding to first yielding ($A = 1.8$) or ultimate capacity ($A = 2.7$) of the maximum-moment section of the composite beam. It may be designated as the live-load factor of safety:

$$\text{LLFS} = A(1 + C_{mc} + C_{mi}C_s) - (C_{mc} + C_{mi}) \qquad (3\text{-}7)$$

The principle of equal strength requires that this multiple should be able to move into the position of maximum moment without a breakdown of composite action. Accordingly, the live-load factor of safety is a constant quantity for any one beam. For a simple-span beam, parameters C_{mc}, C_{mi}, and C_s should be computed at the section of maximum positive moment (always near mid-span). For a continuous beam, the live-load factor of safety should be computed for all sections of maximum positive and maximum negative moment,[1] and the smallest resulting value should be used for the design of shear connectors throughout the beam. Thus for any particular beam, only the parameter C_v is a variable quantity in Eq. (3-6).

Some numerical values of the factor of safety are listed in Table 5-5 for the special case of no temporary supports and no superimposed dead loads; i.e., $C_{mc} = C_v = 0$. The values in Table 5-5 represent the maximum factors of safety. If superimposed dead loads are present, the required factors of safety are always smaller than the values in Table 5-5. It can be seen that the factor of safety against first yielding is always smaller than 4.0 and that for practical combinations of C_s, C_{mi}, and

---

[1] If the negative moments are resisted by the steel section alone, it is sufficiently accurate to evaluate the live-load factor of safety for the negative moment sections from Eq. (3-7) by setting $C_{mc} = 0$ and $C_s = 1.0$. Ordinarily, the live-load factor of safety for the negative-moment sections is higher than for the positive-moment sections and, therefore, does not govern the design of shear connectors.

$A = 2.7$, a factor of safety equal approximately to 4.0 is quite common. *An upper limit of FS = 4.0 is recommended for Eq. (3-6).*

3-6. Spacing of Connectors

The aggregate capacity of all connectors located at one transverse cross section of a beam must be equal to the total horizontal shear divided by the pitch. Thus the required pitch, or spacing parallel to the beam axis, of connectors may be determined as[1]

$$p = \frac{NQ}{S} \qquad (3\text{-}8)$$

where p = spacing, or pitch, of connectors in the direction of beam axis, in.

N = number of connectors at one transverse beam cross section

Q = capacity of one connector computed from Eq. (3-2)

S = horizontal shear computed from Eq. (3-1)

Detailing. The following limitations are recommended for detailing of shear connectors:

1. The spacing p of connectors should not be greater than 24 in.

2. The clear distance between the edge of the beam and the edge of the shear connectors should not be less than 1 in.

3. The clear depth of concrete cover over the top of shear connectors should not be less than 1 in.

4. The connectors should extend at least 2 in. above the bottom of the main body of the slab.

3-7. Design of Connecting Welds

For granular-flux-filled welded studs, no design of welds is required because the stud welding process always furnishes a

---

[1] If the design of shear connectors is based on the requirement that composite action should be retained up to first yielding of the steel beams, the required spacing can be computed directly from the useful capacity as follows:

$$p = \frac{NQ_{uc}}{S_{Dc} + (33{,}000 - f_{DL}/f_{LL})S_{LL}}$$

where S_{Dc} and S_{LL} are the horizontal shears caused by composite dead load and by live load, respectively, and f_{DL} and f_{LL} are the maximum unit stresses in the beam due to dead and live loads, respectively, at the point of the maximum positive moment.

weld having the minimum cross-sectional area equal to the cross section of the stud. Fatigue tests of bare studs have shown an excellent performance of both the weld and the stud under full reversal of loading.

The connecting welds for channel and spiral connectors should be designed in accordance with the AASHO requirements for the design of welds. The shear capacity of all welds on one connector corresponding to the allowable shear stress for the welds must be at least equal to the resistance value of the shear connector Q at working load. The reversal of the live-load stresses should be considered in the design of welds.

3-8. Comparison of Various Types of Shear Connectors

Several types of shear connectors have been proposed and used. Unfortunately, as a result of insufficient knowledge of their behavior, the various types are not designed on a common basis. It is difficult, therefore, to compare objectively the efficiencies of the various types of connectors.

Comparable test data are available for three types of shear connectors now in common use: granular-flux-filled welded stud, flexible-channel shear connector and spiral shear connector. These three types may be compared on the basis of their useful capacities. Two connectors having the same useful capacity are equivalent and may be used interchangeably.

Spiral connectors welded to the top flanges of girders serve as shear connectors in this Ohio Turnpike bridge.

The number of studs having the same useful capacity as a channel connector may be determined from Eqs. (3-3) and (3-4). The numbers of studs necessary to replace 1 in. of channels of various sizes are listed in Table 5-6.

The number of studs having the same useful capacity as one turn of spiral connector may be determined from Eqs. (3-3) and (3-5). The numbers of studs necessary to replace one turn of spirals of various types are listed in Table 5-7 for $f'_c = 3{,}000$ psi.

Tables 5-6 and 5-7 give the numbers of studs which furnish equally strong shear connection as 1 in. of channel or one turn of spiral. Thus, if the design is made for channel shear connectors, the equivalent design in granular-flux-filled welded studs may be obtained simply by replacing every inch of channel by the number of studs given in Table 5-6. Similarly, if the design is made for spiral shear connectors, the equivalent design in the flux-filled studs may be obtained simply by replacing every turn of spiral by the number of studs given in Table 5-7.

3-9. Granular-flux-filled Welded Studs

One of the simplest and most versatile connectors on the market is the granular-flux-filled welded stud, shown schematically in Fig. 3-2. It is a short length of round steel bar welded to the I beam at one end and having an upset head at the other end.

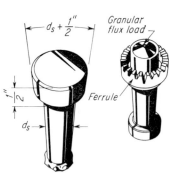

FIG. 3-2. Granular-flux-filled welded stud.

The stud resists horizontal shear by bending; the upset head of the stud prevents relative movements of the slab in the vertical direction.

The studs are available in sizes from $\frac{1}{2}$ to 1 in. in diameter and from 2 to 8 in. or more in length. However, in the interest of standardization and reduction of cost, $\frac{3}{4}$- and $\frac{7}{8}$-in.-diameter studs with an in-place length of 4 in. are recommended.[1] The weights of studs of various sizes are listed in Table 5-8. The weight of studs having an in-place length different from those listed in Table 5-8

[1] Before welding, the studs are slightly longer than after welding. For example, the $\frac{3}{4}$-in. stud 4 in. long in place is $4\frac{3}{16}$ in. long before welding.

may be computed as the weight of a length listed plus the weight of the differential length of the shaft.

The principal advantages of granular-flux-filled welded studs are the ease and speed with which they can be welded to the I beams. Studs are end-welded in 1 sec or less with a lightweight, portable stud-welding gun, which can be operated by a semi-skilled worker. An electric arc, created between the stud and

Stud shear connectors are easily and swiftly welded in place in shop (*left*) or field (*right*).

the flange of the steel beam, melts the end of the stud and a corresponding spot on the flange. After a preset arcing period, a spring in the welding tool automatically plunges the stud into the molten pool of metal, completing the weld. The area of the pool is controlled by an arc shield, or ferrule; one ferrule is used with each weld. The joint obtained is a true metal arc weld stronger than the steel of the stud itself. Portable equipment permits fastening of studs with equal ease in the shop or at the construction site.

For electric-arc stud welding, the welding end of the stud is specially prepared and filled with granular flux. A porcelain ferrule is supplied for use around the base of each stud to shield and control the arc and to concentrate the heat of the arc in the weld area. The ferrule also acts as a mold or dam to control the flow of molten metal and restrict it to the weld area. Experience has shown that consistently sound stud welds cannot be obtained without the use of a ferrule.

From the viewpoint of a designer, these studs offer several advantages. Since an individual stud is a relatively small unit, so that several studs are usually required at the same transverse cross section, the use of studs introduces flexibility of design usually impractical with other types of connectors. The flexibility of layout of stud connectors is especially helpful whenever the placement of the slab reinforcement presents a problem.

The welding process described largely eliminates the warping of the steel beams observed with other types of connectors. The shape of the studs permits a more satisfactory compaction of concrete around the connector than most other shapes of connectors used at present.

Minimum Transverse Spacing. To permit welding of studs, the gap between the heads of two adjacent connectors should not be less than 0.50 in. The diameter of the stud head is standardized at $d_s + 0.5$ in. where d_s is the stud diameter (Fig. 3-2). Therefore, the distance center to center of two adjacent studs should not be less than the stud diameter plus 1.0 in.

3-10. Mechanical Properties of the Stud Steel

The stud is made of AISI 1015, 1017 or 1020 cold-drawn steel, which corresponds approximately to ASTM Designation A-108, having the following physical properties:

> Tensile strength, min psi 65,000
> Yield point, min psi 50,000
> Elongation, min per cent 20
> Reduction of area, min per cent 55

3-11. Test Data

Comprehensive push-out tests of stud shear connectors were carried out for the purpose of determining the load-slip characteristics and the useful capacities. Studs having diameters ranging from $\frac{1}{2}$ to $1\frac{1}{4}$ in. and heights ranging from 2 to 8.5 in. were tested. The push-out tests have proved the stud a reliable shear connector. The results of the push-out tests may be found in Refs. 3 and 5 listed in Chap. 6, Art. 6-1.

In addition to the push-out tests, fatigue tests were carried out on bare studs. The fatigue tests have shown conclusively that repeated loading is not a limiting factor in the design of granular-flux-filled welded studs. The fatigue tests are reported in Ref. 7 and in the discussion of Ref. 3, Art. 6-1.

3-12. Effect of Height-to-diameter Ratio

The useful capacity of a stud shear connector is given by Eq. (3-3a) or (3-3b). Since a stud is essentially a steel dowel embedded in concrete and loaded with a transverse load at the welded end, the useful capacity of a stud connector increases with the increasing length if the ratio of the stud length to the stud diameter is relatively small. If, however, the ratio of the stud length to the stud diameter is relatively large, the useful capacity is independent of the stud length.

Accordingly, it is safe to design all granular-flux-filled welded studs with height-to-diameter ratio equal to or larger than 4.2 according to Eq. (3-3a), independently of the stud length. On the other hand, the useful capacity of studs with the height-to-diameter ratio smaller than 4.2 is given by Eq. (3-3b), including the effect of the stud length.

3-13. Example. Design of Shear Connectors

Design Data

Span $= 56$ ft

Distance center to center bearings $= 55$ ft

Beam spacing $= 6$ ft 9 in.

Live load $=$ H20-S16-44

Live-load distribution for moment $= 6.75/5.5 = 1.227$

DLs $= 687.1$ lb per ft

DLc $= 184.1$ lb per ft

$M_{LL} = 562.2$ kip-ft

$M_{Ds} = 69.6$ kip-ft

$M_{Dc} = 259.8$ kip-ft

$f'_c = 3,000$ psi

$f_c = 1,200$ psi

$f_s = 18,000$ psi

$n = 10$

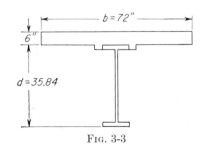

FIG. 3-3

Assume a 36 WF 150 with $I_c = 18,700$ in.[4], $m = 457.1$ in.[3], $S_{bs} = 502.9$ in.[3], and $S_{bc} = 661.7$ in.[3].

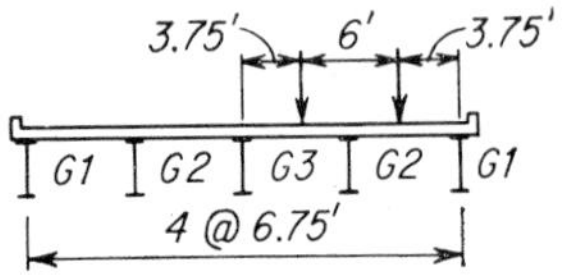

At the center line of bearing, the distribution of load to girder $G2$ is

$$\frac{3.75}{6.75} + \frac{3.75}{6.75} = 1.111 \text{ wheels}$$

Fig. 3-4. Distribution of wheel loads at reaction to $G2$.

Vertical Shear

At the center line of bearing, with a 16-kip wheel over the bearing, a 16 kip wheel 14 ft on the span and a 4-kip wheel another 14 ft away:

$$V_{LL} = 16 \times 1.111 + (16 \times 41 + 4 \times 27)\frac{1.227}{55} = \quad 34.82 \text{ kips}$$

$$\text{Impact} = \frac{50}{55 + 120} \times 34.82 = \quad 9.67$$

$$V_{LL} + \text{impact} = \quad 44.49$$

$$V_{Dc} = 0.1841 \times 55 \times \tfrac{1}{2} = \quad 5.06$$

$$\text{Max } V_c = \quad 49.55 \text{ kips}$$

At 7 ft from the center line of bearing:

$$V_{LL} = (16 \times 48 + 16 \times 34 + 4 \times 20)\frac{1.227}{55} = \quad 31.05 \text{ kips}$$

$$\text{Impact} = \frac{50}{48 + 125} \times 31.05 = \quad 8.97$$

$$V_{LL} + \text{impact} = \quad 40.02$$

$$V_{Dc} = 5.06 - 0.1841 \times 7 = \quad 3.77$$

$$\text{Max } V_c = \quad 43.79 \text{ kips}$$

For minimum shear at this section:

$$V_{LL} = -(16 \times 7)\frac{1.227}{55} = -\ 2.50 \text{ kips}$$

$$\text{Impact} = 0.30 \times -2.50 = -\ 0.75$$

$$V_{LL} + \text{impact} = -\ 3.25$$

$$V_{Dc} = \quad 3.77$$

$$\text{Min } V_c = \quad 0.52 \text{ kips}$$

At 14 ft from the center line of bearing:

$$V_{LL} = (16 \times 41 + 16 \times 27 + 4 \times 13)\frac{1.227}{55} = \quad 25.43 \text{ kips}$$

$$\text{Impact} = 0.30 \times 25.43 = \quad \underline{7.63}$$

$$V_{LL} + \text{impact} = \quad 33.06$$

$$V_{Dc} = 5.06 - 0.1841 \times 14 = \quad \underline{2.48}$$

$$\text{Max } V_c = \quad 35.54 \text{ kips}$$

For minimum shear at this section:

$$V_{LL} = -(16 \times 14)\frac{1.227}{55} = - \ 5.00 \text{ kips}$$

$$\text{Impact} = 0.30 \times -5.00 = - \ \underline{1.50}$$

$$V_{LL} + \text{impact} = - \ 6.50$$

$$V_{Dc} = \quad \underline{2.48}$$

$$\text{Min } V_c = - \ 4.02 \text{ kips}$$

At 21 ft from the center line of bearing:

$$V_{LL} = (16 \times 34 + 16 \times 20 + 4 \times 6)\frac{1.227}{55} = \quad 19.81 \text{ kips}$$

$$\text{Impact} = 0.30 \times 19.81 = \quad \underline{5.94}$$

$$V_{LL} + \text{impact} = \quad 25.75$$

$$V_{Dc} = 5.06 - 0.1841 \times 21 = \quad \underline{1.19}$$

$$\text{Max } V_c = \quad 26.94 \text{ kips}$$

For minimum shear 21 ft from bearing:

$$V_{LL} = -(16 \times 21 + 16 \times 7)\frac{1.227}{55} = - \ 9.98 \text{ kips}$$

$$\text{Impact} = 0.30 \times -9.98 = - \ \underline{2.99}$$

$$V_{LL} + \text{impact} = -12.97$$

$$V_{Dc} = \quad \underline{1.19}$$

$$\text{Min } V_c = -11.78 \text{ kips}$$

Factors of Safety [from Eq. (3-6)]

$$\text{FS} = \frac{2.7(1 + C_{mc} + C_{mi}C_s) - (C_{mc} + C_{mi}) + C_v}{1 + C_v}$$

$$= \frac{\text{LLFS} + C_v}{1 + C_v}$$

$$C_{mc} = \frac{M_{Dc}}{M_{LL}} = \frac{69.6}{562.2} = 0.124$$

$$C_{mi} = \frac{M_{Ds}}{M_{LL}} = \frac{259.8}{562.2} = 0.462$$

$$C_s = \frac{S_{bc}}{S_{bs}} = \frac{661.7}{502.9} = 1.316$$

$$\text{LLFS} = 2.7(1 + 0.124 + 0.462 \times 1.316) - (0.124 + 0.462)$$
$$= 4.09$$

At the center line of bearing:

$$C_v = \frac{V_{Dc}}{V_{LL} + \text{impact}} = \frac{5.06}{44.49} = 0.10$$

$$\text{FS} = \frac{4.09 + 0.10}{1 + 0.10} = 3.81$$

At 7 ft from the center line of bearing:

$$C_v = \frac{3.77}{40.02} = 0.09$$

$$\text{FS} = \frac{4.09 + 0.09}{1 + 0.09} = 3.83$$

At 14 ft from the center line of bearing:

$$C_v = \frac{2.48}{33.06} = 0.08$$

$$\text{FS} = \frac{4.09 + 0.08}{1 + 0.08} = 3.86$$

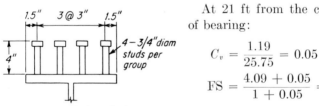

FIG. 3-5. Welded-stud shear connectors.

At 21 ft from the center line of bearing:

$$C_v = \frac{1.19}{25.75} = 0.05$$

$$\text{FS} = \frac{4.09 + 0.05}{1 + 0.05} = 3.94$$

Alternate A. Design of Stud Shear Connectors. Assume four $\frac{3}{4}$-in.-diameter studs per group on the top flange of the 36 WF 150. For these studs, $h_s = 4$ in. The useful capacity of each $\frac{3}{4}$-in.-diameter stud, according to Eq. (3-3a), is

$$Q_{uc} = 330 \times 0.75^2 \sqrt{3,000} = 10,200 \text{ lb}$$
$$4Q_{uc} = 40.8 \text{ kips}$$

From Eqs. (3-1) and (3-8), the pitch for groups of four $\frac{3}{4}$-in. studs should be

$$p = \frac{NQ}{S} = \frac{I_c}{mV_c}\frac{4Q_{uc}}{\text{FS}} = \frac{18,700}{457}\frac{40.8}{\text{FS}}\frac{1}{V_c} = \frac{1,669}{V_c \times \text{FS}}$$

At the center line of bearing, the required spacing of stud groups is

$$p = \frac{1,669}{49.6 \times 3.81} = 8.83 \text{ in.}$$

At 7 ft from the center line of bearing:

$$p = \frac{1,669}{43.8 \times 3.83} = 9.93 \text{ in.}$$

At 14 ft from the center line of bearing:

$$p = \frac{1,669}{35.5 \times 3.86} = 12.18 \text{ in.}$$

At 21 ft from the center line of bearing:

$$p = \frac{1,669}{26.9 \times 3.94} = 15.75 \text{ in.}$$

Actual spacing to be used, based on these calculations, is shown in Fig. 3-6.

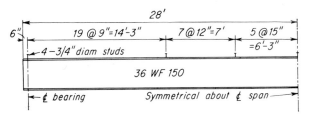

FIG. 3-6. Spacing of stud shear connectors.

Alternate B. Design of Channel Shear Connectors. Assume 4-in. 5.4-lb channel shear connectors attached with $\frac{3}{16}$-in. welds to the top flange of the 36 WF 150. From Eq. (3-4) and Table 5-4b

$$Q_{uc} = 180(0.413 + 0.5 \times 0.180)10 \sqrt{3,000}$$
$$Q_{uc} = 50,100 \text{ lb}$$

Use $\frac{3}{16}$-in. fillet weld on toe and heel of the channel. The pitch, or spacing of channels, can be determined from

FIG. 3-7. Channel shear connector.

$$p = \frac{I_c}{mV_c}\frac{Q_{uc}}{\text{FS}} = \frac{18,700}{457.1}\frac{50.1}{\text{FS}}\frac{1}{V_c} = \frac{2,050}{V_c \times \text{FS}}$$

With A_w the weld area per inch of weld and f_w the allowable stress in weld, the required length of weld is

$$L_w = \frac{Q_{uc}}{A_w f_w \times \text{FS}}\left(\frac{\max V_c - \min V_c \times \frac{1}{2}}{\max V_c}\right)$$

$$= \frac{50.1}{0.188 \times 0.707 \times 10.0 \times \text{FS}}\left(\frac{\max V_c - \min V_c \times \frac{1}{2}}{\max V_c}\right)$$

$$= \frac{37.7}{\text{FS}}\left(\frac{\max V_c - \min V_c \times \frac{1}{2}}{\max V_c}\right)$$

At the center line of bearing, the required pitch and weld length are, respectively,

$$p = \frac{2,050}{49.6 \times 3.81} = 11.88 \text{ in.}$$

$$L_w = \frac{37.7}{3.81} \times \frac{49.6 - 5.06 \times \frac{1}{2}}{49.6} = 9.39 \text{ in.}$$

At 7 ft from the center line of bearing:

$$p = \frac{2,050}{43.8 \times 3.83} = 12.21 \text{ in.}$$

$$L_w = \frac{37.7}{3.83} \times \frac{43.8 - 0.52 \times \frac{1}{2}}{43.8} = 9.79 \text{ in.}$$

At 14 ft from the center line of bearing:

$$p = \frac{2,050}{35.5 \times 3.86} = 14.96 \text{ in.}$$

$$L_w = \frac{37.7}{3.86} \times \frac{35.5 - (-4.02) \times \frac{1}{2}}{35.5} = 10.32 \text{ in.}$$

At 21 ft from the center line of bearing:

$$p = \frac{2,050}{26.9 \times 3.94} = 19.33 \text{ in.}$$

$$L_w = \frac{37.7}{3.94} \times \frac{26.9 - (-11.78) \times \frac{1}{2}}{26.9} = 11.68 \text{ in.}$$

To prevent transverse bending of the channel, the $\frac{3}{16}$-in. weld should be extended full width at toe and heel:

$$L_w = 10 \times 2 = 20 \text{ in.} > 11.7 \text{ in.}$$

The actual spacing of channels to be used is shown in Fig. 3-8.

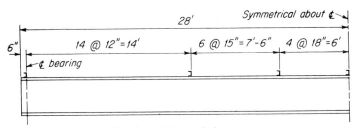

FIG. 3-8. Spacing of channel shear connectors.

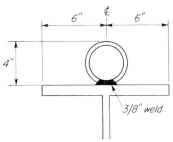

FIG. 3-9. Spiral shear connector.

Alternate C. Design of Spiral Shear Connectors. Assume $\frac{3}{4}$-in.-diameter spiral shear connectors and $\frac{3}{8}$-in. welds.

$$Q_{uc} = 3,840 \times 0.75 \sqrt[4]{3,000}$$
$$Q_{uc} = 21,300 \text{ lb}$$

The pitch and weld length can be determined from

$$p = \frac{I_c}{mV_c} \frac{Q_{uc}}{\text{FS}} = \frac{18,700}{457.1} \frac{21.3}{\text{FS}} \frac{1}{V_c} = \frac{873}{V_c \times \text{FS}}$$

$$L_w = \frac{Q_{uc}}{A_w f_w \times \text{FS}} \frac{\max V_c - \min V_c \times \frac{1}{2}}{\max V_c}$$

$$= \frac{21.3}{0.375 \times 0.707 \times 10 \times \text{FS}} \frac{\max V_c - \min V_c \times \frac{1}{2}}{\max V_c}$$

$$= \frac{8.04}{\text{FS}} \frac{\max V_c - \min V_c \times \frac{1}{2}}{\max V_c}$$

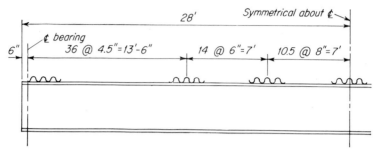

FIG. 3-10. Spacing of spiral shear connectors.

At the center line of bearing:

$$p = \frac{873}{49.6 \times 3.81} = 4.61 \text{ in.}$$

$$L_w = \frac{8.04}{3.81} \times \frac{49.6 - 5.06 \times \frac{1}{2}}{49.6} = 2.02 \text{ in.}$$

At 7 ft from the center line of bearing:

$$p = \frac{873}{43.8 \times 3.83} = 5.20 \text{ in.}$$

$$L_w = \frac{8.04}{3.83} \times \frac{43.8 - 0.52 \times \frac{1}{2}}{43.8} = 2.08 \text{ in.}$$

At 14 ft from the center line of bearing:

$$p = \frac{873}{35.5 \times 3.86} = 6.37 \text{ in.}$$

$$L_w = \frac{8.04}{3.86} \times \frac{35.5 - (-4.02) \times \frac{1}{2}}{35.5} = 2.20 \text{ in.}$$

At 21 ft from the center line of bearing:

$$p = \frac{873}{26.9 \times 3.94} = 8.24 \text{ in.}$$

$$L_w = \frac{8.04}{3.94} \times \frac{26.9 - (-11.78) \times \frac{1}{2}}{26.9} = 2.48 \text{ in.}$$

Use a 2-in.-long weld on each side of the spiral at each pitch point.

CHAPTER 4

DESIGN OF COMPOSITE BEAMS
AND SHEAR CONNECTORS

The design of composite beams and shear connectors will be illustrated by several examples:

1. Simple-span bridge with rolled beams, no shoring during concreting of slab; length 56 ft

2. Simple-span bridge with rolled beams and cover plates, no shoring; length 80 ft

3. Simple-span bridge with welded plate girders, no shoring; length 80 ft

4. Simple-span bridge with rolled beams, cover plates, and shoring; length 80 ft

5. Three-span continuous bridge with rolled beams and cover plates, no shoring; spans 80.5-100-80.5 ft

6. Four-span continuous bridge with welded plate girders, no shoring; spans 116-154-154-116 ft

4-1. Design Criteria for Examples

The bridges in Examples 4-1 through 4-5 are five-girder structures with a 6-in. slab placed with bottom flush with the top surfaces of the girders. A typical half section is shown in Fig. 4-1. The drawing indicates a construction joint between the slab and the curb; the curb and the sidewalk are cast after the slab is cured.

The bridge in Example 4-6 is a four-girder structure with a 6.5-in. slab placed flush with the top surfaces of the girders. Typical half section with all details is shown together with the calculations in Fig. 4-16.

All bridges are designed for standard H20-S16-44 trucks, in accordance with the 1957 edition of the "Standard Specifications for Highway Bridges" adopted by the American Association of State Highway Officials (AASHO). The designs are made for 3,000-psi concrete and structural-grade steel; accordingly, the allowable stresses are $f_c = 1,200$ psi and $f_s = 18,000$ psi, respectively. The modulus of elasticity of steel is $E_s = 29,000,000$ psi, and the modular ratio is $n = 10$. It is assumed that the deck forms act as simple beams between the girders and that the dead loads added after the deck is cured—safety curbs, sidewalks, handrails, and future paving—are distributed by the deck equally to all girders.

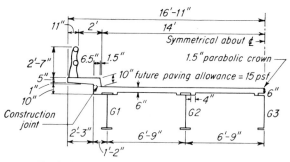

FIG. 4-1. Typical half section of bridge (Examples 4-1 to 4-5).

Each example involves selection of the steel cross section, computation of stresses, and design of shear connectors for girder $G2$. In addition, Example 4-2 includes computation of dead-load deflections, Example 4-3 computation of shrinkage stresses, and Example 4-4 computation of live-load deflections.

Examples 4-1, 4-2, 4-4, and 4-5 illustrate the use of 36 WF 150 beams for various conditions of composite construction. The designer should be able to arrive from these examples at the approximate economy to be gained with each type of construction, depending on the costs and practice in his own locality. Example 4-3 should offer a reasonable comparison of welded girders with cover-plated rolled sections.

Example 4-1. Simple-span Bridge with Rolled Beams, No Shoring (girder $G2$, Fig. 4-1)

Design data

Length = 56 ft 0 in.

Distance center to center bearings = 55 ft 0 in.

Live load is H20-S16-44

Live-load distribution to $G2$ = 6.75/5.5 = 1.227

Dead loads on composite beam $G2$:

$$\text{Two rails} = 20 \text{ psf} \times \tfrac{2}{5} = 8.0 \text{ lb per ft}$$

Two sidewalks = $2.25 \times 5.5/12$

$$@ 150 \text{ lb per cu ft} \times \tfrac{2}{5} = 61.9$$

Two curbs = 0.604×0.833 @ 150 lb per cu ft $\times \tfrac{2}{5} = 30.2$

Future paving = 28.00 @ 15 psf $\times \tfrac{1}{5} = 84.0$

$$\text{Dead load on composite beam} = 184.1 \text{ lb per ft}$$

Dead loads on steel beam:

Deck slab = 6.75×0.500 @ 150 lb per cu ft = 506.3 lb per ft

Slab coping, or haunch = 0.667×0.083 @ 150

$$\text{lb per cu ft} = \quad 8.3$$

Deflection = 1.667×0.050 @ 150 lb per cu ft = 12.5

$$\text{Diaphragms} = \quad 10.0$$

$$\text{Dead load on steel beam less beam weight} = \overline{537.1} \text{ lb per ft}$$

$$\text{Estimated girder weight} = 150.0$$

$$\text{Dead load on steel beam alone} = \overline{687.1} \text{ lb per ft}$$

Selection of Trial Section. The method outlined in Art. 2-11 will be followed.

For a uniform dead load of 687 lb per ft, the maximum bending moment in the unshored steel beam is

$$M_{Ds} = \frac{0.687}{8} \times 55^2$$

$$= 259.8 \text{ kip-ft}$$

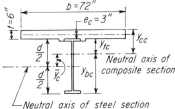

Fig. 4-2. Design section for girder $G2$ (Example 4-1).

To carry this moment, the steel beam should have a section modulus of $259.8 \times {}^{12}\!/_{18} = 173.2$.

The composite beam must carry a dead-load moment equal to

$$M_{Dc} = \frac{0.1841}{8} \times 55^2 = 69.6 \text{ kip-ft}$$

For this moment, a section modulus of $69.6 \times 12\%_8 = 46.4$ is required.

The live-load and impact moments are

$$M_{LL} = 717.2 \times 1.227 \times \tfrac{1}{2} = 440 \text{ kip-ft}$$

where 717.2 is the maximum moment for truck loading on a 55-ft span, 1.227 is the load distribution factor for a wheel load, and $\tfrac{1}{2}$ is a conversion factor for changing the truck axle load to wheel load.

$$\text{Impact } M = \frac{50}{55 + 125} \times 440 = 122 \text{ kip-ft}$$

$$M_{LL} + I = 562 \text{ kip-ft}$$

The section modulus required is $562 \times 12\%_8 = 375$.

If a steel beam were to carry the full load unassisted by the concrete slab, it would need a section modulus equal to $173 + 46 + 375 = 594$. The steel section for the composite beam, however, will be smaller.

Assume a 36 WF 150, with area $A_s = 44.16$ in.², depth $d = 35.84$ in., moment of inertia $I_s = 9,012$ in.⁴, and section modulus $S_s = 502.9$ in.³. The distance e_c from the top surface of the beam to the center of gravity of the concrete slab is 3 in. Hence,

$$\frac{e_c}{d} = \frac{3}{35.84} = 0.0837$$

Other constants needed are

$$\frac{S_s}{A_s} = \frac{502.9}{44.16} = 11.39 \text{ in.}$$

factor for sustained loads:

$$k_{Dc} = 3$$

factor for temporary loads:

$$k_{LL} = 1$$

transformed area of slab for sustained loads:

$$A_c = \frac{bt}{kn} = \frac{72 \times 6}{3 \times 10} = 14.40 \text{ in.}^2$$

and for temporary loads:

$$A_c = \frac{72 \times 6}{1 \times 10} = 43.2 \text{ in.}^2$$

Similarly, for sustained loads:

$$K_c = \frac{A_c}{A_c + A_s} = \frac{14.40}{14.40 + 44.16} = 0.246$$

and for temporary loads:

$$K_c = \frac{43.20}{43.20 + 44.16} = 0.495$$

From Fig. 5-1, $S_{bc}/A_s d = 0.388$ and 0.425 for the two values of K_c.

The factors computed will now be substituted in Eq. (2-7c) to find the required area of the steel section:

Steel area required for dead loads on steel beam alone is

$$A_{Ds} = \frac{M_{Ds} A_s}{f_b S_s} = \frac{173.2}{11.39} = 15.21 \text{ in.}^2$$

Steel area required for dead loads on composite beam:

$$A_{Dc} = \frac{M_{Dc}}{f_b} \frac{A_s d}{S_{bc}} \frac{1}{d} = \frac{46.4}{0.388 \times 35.84} = 3.34$$

Steel area required to resist live loads:

$$A_{LL} = \frac{M_{LL}}{f_b} \frac{A_s d}{S_{bc}} \frac{1}{d} = \frac{374.8}{0.425 \times 35.84} = 24.61$$

$$\text{Required total steel area } A_s = \overline{43.16 \text{ in.}^2}$$

Try a 36 WF 150, with $A_s = 44.16$ in.^{2}.

Properties of Trial Section. Composite section with $k = 3$ and applying (Eq. 2-3):

$$K_c = \frac{A_c}{A_c + A_s} = 0.246$$

$$\bar{y}_c = (y_{ts} + e_c)K_c = (17.92 + 3)0.246 = 5.14 \text{ in.}$$

$$I_c = (y_{ts} + e_c)\bar{y}_c A_s + I_s + A_c \frac{t^2}{12} = 20.92 \times 5.14 \times 44.16$$

$$+ 9,012 + \frac{14.40 \times 6^2}{12} = 13,810 \text{ in.}^4$$

$$y_{tc} = y_{ts} - \bar{y}_c = 17.92 - 5.14 = 12.78 \text{ in.}$$

$$S_{tc} = \frac{I_c}{y_{tc}} = \frac{13,810}{12.78} = 1,081 \text{ in.}^3$$

$$y_{bc} = y_{bs} + \bar{y}_c = 17.92 + 5.14 = 23.06 \text{ in.}$$

$$S_{bc} = \frac{I_c}{y_{bc}} = \frac{13,810}{12.78} = 599 \text{ in.}^3$$

$$y_{cc} = \frac{d}{2} - \bar{y}_c + t = 17.92 - 5.14 + 6 = 18.78 \text{ in.}$$

$$S_{cc} = \frac{I_c}{y_{cc}} = \frac{13,810}{18.78} = 735 \text{ in.}^3$$

Composite section with $k = 1$:

$$K_c = \frac{A_c}{A_c + A_s} = 0.495$$

$$\bar{y}_c = 20.92 \times 0.495 = 10.34 \text{ in.}$$

$$I_c = 10.34 \times 20.92 \times 44.16 + 9,012 + \frac{43.20 \times 6^2}{12}$$

$$= 18,700 \text{ in.}^4$$

$$y_{tc} = 17.92 - 10.34 = 7.58 \text{ in.}$$

$$S_{tc} = \frac{18,700}{7.58} = 2,467 \text{ in.}^3$$

$$y_{bc} = 17.92 + 10.34 = 28.26 \text{ in.}$$

$$S_{bc} = \frac{18,700}{28.26} = 662 \text{ in.}^3$$

$$y_{cc} = 17.92 - 10.34 + 6 = 13.58 \text{ in.}$$

$$S_{cc} = \frac{18,700}{13.58} = 1,377 \text{ in.}^3$$

The statical moment of the transformed concrete area about the neutral axis of the composite section

$$m = A_c(y_{tc} + e_c) = 43.20(7.58 + 3) = 457 \text{ in.}^3$$

Stresses [Eqs. (2-3k), (2-3l), and (2-3m)]

	Concrete, f_c, ksi	Steel top flange, f_t ksi	Steel bottom flange, f_b, ksi
Dead load on steel beam alone (DLs)	0	$\dfrac{259.8 \times 12}{502.9} = 6.20$	$\dfrac{3,118}{502.9} = 6.20$
Dead load on composite section (DLc), $kn = 30$	$\dfrac{69.6 \times 12}{735 \times 30} = 0.04$	$\dfrac{835.2}{1,081} = 0.77$	$\dfrac{835.2}{599} = 1.39$
Live load on composite section (LL), $kn = 10$	$\dfrac{562 \times 12}{1,377 \times 10} = 0.49$	$\dfrac{6,746}{2,467} = 2.73$	$\dfrac{6,746}{662} = 10.19$
	0.53	9.70	17.78

Shear Connector Spacing

The useful capacity of each ¾-in.-diameter stud, according to

Eq. (3-3a), is

$$Q_{uc} = 330 \times 0.75^2 \sqrt{3,000} = 10,200 \text{ lb}$$
$$4Q_{uc} = 40.8 \text{ kips}$$

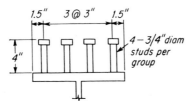

FIG. 4-3. Location of studs on girder flange.

From Eq. (3-6), the factor of safety is

$$\text{FS} = \frac{2.7(1 + C_{mc} + C_{mi}C_s) - (C_{mc} + C_{mi}) + C_v}{1 + C_v}$$

$$= \frac{\text{LLFS} + C_v}{1 + C_v}$$

$$C_{mc} = \frac{M_{Dc}}{M_{LL}} = \frac{69.6}{562.2} = 0.124$$

$$C_{mi} = \frac{M_{Ds}}{M_{LL}} = \frac{259.8}{562.2} = 0.462$$

$$C_s = \frac{S_{bc}}{S_{bs}} = \frac{661.7}{502.9} = 1.316$$

$$\text{LLFS} = 2.7(1 + 0.124 + 0.462 \times 1.316) - (0.124 + 0.462)$$
$$= 4.09$$

From Eqs. (3-1) and (3-8), the pitch for groups of four ¾-in. studs should be

$$p = \frac{NQ}{S} = \frac{I_c}{mV_c} \frac{4Q_{uc}}{\text{FS}} = \frac{18,700}{457} \frac{40.8}{\text{FS}} \frac{1}{V_c} = \frac{1,669}{V_c \times \text{FS}}$$

Distribution of wheels at reaction:

$$\frac{3.75}{6.75} + \frac{3.75}{6.75} = 1.111 \text{ wheels}$$

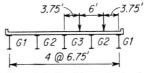

FIG. 4-4. Position of wheels for end shear.

At the center line of bearing, with a 16-kip wheel over the bearing, a 16-kip wheel 14 ft on the span and a 4-kip wheel another 14 ft away:

$$V_{LL} = 16 \times 1.111 + (16 \times 41 + 4 \times 27) \frac{1.227}{55} = 34.82 \text{ kips}$$

$$\text{Impact} = \frac{50}{55 + 125} \times 34.82 = 9.67$$

$$V_{LL} + \text{impact} = 44.49 \text{ kips}$$
$$V_{Dc} = 0.1841 \times 55 \times \tfrac{1}{2} = 5.06$$
$$V_c = 49.55 \text{ kips}$$

$$C_v = \frac{V_{Dc}}{(V_{LL} + \text{impact})} = 0.10$$

From Eq. (3-6), we find

$$\text{FS} = \frac{\text{LLFS} + C_v}{1 + C_v} = \frac{4.09 + 0.10}{1 + 0.10} = 3.81$$

The maximum pitch of the stud groups then is

$$p = \frac{1,669}{V_c \times \text{FS}} = \frac{1,669}{49.6 \times 3.81} = 8.83 \text{ in.}$$

At 7 ft from the center line of bearing:

$$V_{LL} = (16 \times 48 + 16 \times 34 + 4 \times 20) \frac{1.227}{55} = 31.05 \text{ kips}$$

$$\text{Impact} = \frac{50}{48 + 125} \times 31.05 = 8.97$$

$$V_{LL} + \text{impact} = 40.02 \text{ kips}$$
$$V_{Dc} = 5.06 - 0.1841 \times 7 = 3.77$$
$$V_c = 43.79 \text{ kips}$$

$$C_v = \frac{3.77}{40.02} = 0.09$$

$$\text{FS} = \frac{4.09 + 0.09}{1 + 0.09} = 3.83$$

$$p = \frac{1,669}{43.8 \times 3.83} = 9.93 \text{ in.}$$

At 14 ft from the center line of bearing:

$$V_{LL} = (16 \times 41 + 16 \times 27 + 4 \times 13) \frac{1.227}{55} = 25.43 \text{ kips}$$

$$\text{Impact} = 0.30 \times 25.43 = 7.63$$

$$V_{LL} + \text{impact} = 33.06 \text{ kips}$$
$$V_{Dc} = 5.06 - 0.1841 \times 14 = 2.48$$
$$V_c = 35.54 \text{ kips}$$

$$C_v = \frac{2.48}{33.06} = 0.08$$

$$FS = \frac{4.09 + 0.08}{1 + 0.08} = 3.86$$

$$p = \frac{1,669}{35.5 \times 3.86} = 12.18 \text{ in.}$$

At 21 ft from the center line of bearing:

$$V_{LL} = (16 \times 34 + 16 \times 20 + 4 \times 6) \frac{1.227}{55} = 19.81 \text{ kips}$$

$$\text{Impact} = 0.30 \times 19.81 = \underline{5.94}$$

$$V_{LL} + \text{impact} = 25.75 \text{ kips}$$

$$V_{Dc} = 5.06 - 0.1841 \times 21 = \underline{1.19}$$

$$V_c = 26.94 \text{ kips}$$

$$C_v = \frac{1.19}{25.75} = 0.05$$

$$FS = \frac{4.09 + 0.05}{1 + 0.05} = 3.94$$

$$p = \frac{1,669}{26.9 \times 3.94} = 15.75 \text{ in.}$$

Final Section

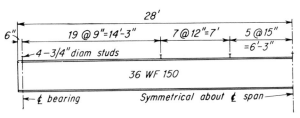

FIG. 4-5. Spacing of shear connectors on $G2$ (Example 4-1).

Example 4-2. Simple-span Bridge with Rolled Beams and Cover Plates, No Shoring (girder $G2$, Fig. 4-1). Two important points concerning the selection of the preliminary section are illustrated in this example:

1. The top-flange stress in the sections selected by the procedure presented in this book is usually several per cent smaller than the allowable stress.

2. If the area of the cover plate approaches or exceeds the area of the flange of the rolled beam, the cover plate selected by

the procedure presented in this book is usually a few per cent larger than required by the allowable stress.

Anticipating such differences, we select, in the following example, the area both of the beam and of the cover plate slightly smaller than indicated by the preliminary design. The resulting stresses in the top and bottom flanges of the steel beam then turn out to be close to the allowable, 18,000 psi.

Dead-load deflections can be calculated by either of two methods: (1) by considering the variation in the moment of inertia and (2) by assuming the larger moment of inertia as constant throughout the beam. As can be shown, there is no appreciable difference in the resulting deflections; therefore, complete calculations are included only for the simpler second method. It should be noted that the weight of the steel beam is not included, because the beams will be in place when grades are set prior to concreting the slab.

Design Data

Length = 80 ft 0 in.

Distance center to center bearings = 79 ft 0 in.

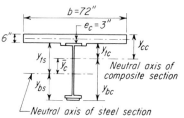

Fig. 4-6. Design section (Example 4-2).

Live load = H20-S16-44

Live-load distribution to $G2$ = 6.75/5.5 = 1.227

Dead load on steel beam plus its weight (see Example 4-1) = 537.1 + 195.0 = 732.1   lb per ft

Dead load on composite beam (see Example 4-1) = 184.1 lb per ft

Selection of Trial Section. Following the method described in Art. 2-12, we first find the maximum bending moments for dead and live loads and the required section modulus for each case:

$$M_{Ds} = \frac{0.732}{8} \times 79^2 = 571 \text{ kip-ft}$$

for which the section modulus required is 380.8 in.³

$$M_{Dc} = \frac{0.1841}{8} \times 79^2 = 143.6 \text{ kip-ft}$$

and the corresponding section modulus is 95.8 in.[3].

$$M_{LL} = 1{,}147 \times \tfrac{1}{2} \times 1.227 = 704 \text{ kip-ft}$$

$$\text{Impact} = \frac{50}{79 + 125} \times 704 = 173 \text{ kip-ft}$$

$$M_{LL} + I = 877 \text{ kip-ft,}$$

requiring a section modulus of 585 in.[3].

Assume a 36 WF 150, with area $A_s = 44.16$ in.[2], depth $d = 35.84$ in., moment of inertia $I_s = 9{,}012$ in.[4], and section modulus $S_s = 502.9$ in.[3]. The following values are computed as in Example 4-1:

$$\frac{e_c}{d} = \frac{3}{35.84} = 0.0837 \qquad \frac{S_s}{A_s} = \frac{502.9}{44.16} = 11.39 \text{ in.}$$

$$k_{Dc} = 3 \qquad\qquad\qquad k_{LL} = 1$$

$$A_c = \frac{bt}{kn} = 14.40 \text{ in.}^2 \qquad A_c = 43.2 \text{ in.}^2$$

$$K_c = \frac{A_c}{A_c + A_s} = 0.246 \qquad K_c = 0.495$$

From Figs. 5-1 and 5-2, for $k = 3$ and 1, respectively,

$$\frac{S_{bc}}{A_s d} = 0.388 \qquad \frac{S_{bc}}{A_s d} = 0.425$$

$$\frac{A_s d}{S_{tc}} = 1.435 \qquad \frac{A_s d}{S_{tc}} = 0.635$$

Applying Eq. (2-8b), we determine the requirements for the area of the steel section:

Top flange:

$$A_{Ds} = \frac{M_{Ds}}{S_s/A_s} = \frac{380.8}{11.39} \qquad\qquad = 33.43 \text{ in.}^2$$

$$A_{Dc} = \frac{M_{Dc}}{d}\frac{A_s d}{S_{tc}} = \frac{95.8 \times 1.435}{35.84} = 3.84$$

$$A_{LL} = \frac{M_{LL}}{d}\frac{A_s d}{S_{tc}} = \frac{585 \times 0.635}{35.84} = 10.35$$

$$\text{Required } A_B = \overline{47.62 \text{ in.}^2}$$

The next step is to compute the area of cover plate from Eq. (2-9):

$$A_{Ds} = \frac{380.8}{11.39} \qquad\qquad = 33.43 \text{ in.}^2$$

$$A_{Dc} = \frac{M_{Dc}}{d} \frac{A_s d}{S_{bc}} = \frac{95.8}{35.84 \times 0.388} = 6.89$$

$$A_{LL} = \frac{M_{LL}}{d} \frac{A_s d}{S_{bc}} = \frac{585}{35.84 \times 0.425} = 38.35$$

$$\text{Required } A_s = \overline{78.67 \text{ in.}^2}$$

Try a 36 WF 150, with area $A_B = 44.16$ in.^{2}. Then the required area of the cover plate A_p is found from Eq. (2-9):

$$\tfrac{1}{2}(78.67 - 44.16) = 17.25 \text{ in.}^2$$

Try a $1\frac{9}{16}$ by $10\frac{1}{2}$ plate, $A_p = 16.41$ in.^{2}.

It should be noted that both the beam area A_B and the cover-plate area A_p were selected smaller than the "required" values.

Properties of Trial Section

Steel section [see Eq. (2-1)]:

$$K_s = \frac{A_p}{A_s} = \frac{A_p}{A_p + A_B} = \frac{16.41}{16.41 + 44.16} = 0.2709$$

$$\bar{y}_s = \tfrac{1}{2}(d + t_p)K_s = \tfrac{1}{2}(35.84 + 1.56)0.2709 = 5.07 \text{ in.}$$

$$I_s = \tfrac{1}{2}(d + t_p)\bar{y}_s A_B + I_B = 18.70 \times 5.07 \times 44.16 + 9{,}012$$
$$= 13{,}200 \text{ in.}^4$$

$$y_{ts} = \frac{d}{2} + \bar{y}_s = 17.92 + 5.07 = 22.99 \text{ in.}$$

$$S_{ts} = \frac{13{,}200}{22.99} = 574 \text{ in.}^3$$

$$y_{bs} = \frac{d}{2} + t_p - \bar{y}_s = 17.92 - 5.07 + 1.56 = 14.41 \text{ in.}$$

$$S_{bs} = \frac{13{,}200}{14.41} = 916 \text{ in.}^3$$

Composite section: With $k = 3$ and using Eq. (2-3), we compute

$$K_c = \frac{A_c}{A_c + A_s} = \frac{14.40}{14.40 + 60.57} = 0.1920$$

$$\bar{y}_c = (y_{ts} + e_c)K_c = (22.99 + 3)0.1920 = 4.99 \text{ in.}$$

$$I_c = \bar{y}_c(y_{ts} + e_c)A_s + I_s + A_c \frac{t^2}{12} = 4.99 \times 25.99 \times 60.57$$

$$+ 13{,}200 + \frac{14.40 \times 6^2}{12} = 21{,}100 \text{ in.}^4$$

$y_{tc} = y_{ts} - \bar{y}_c = 22.99 - 4.99 = 18.00$ in.

$S_{tc} = \dfrac{21{,}100}{18.00} = 1{,}172$ in.^{3}

$y_{bc} = y_{bs} + \bar{y}_c = 14.41 + 4.99 = 19.40$

$S_{bc} = \dfrac{21{,}100}{19.40} = 1{,}088$ in.^{3}

$y_{cc} = y_{tc} + e_c + \dfrac{t}{2} = 18 + 3 + 3 = 24.00$ in.

$S_{cc} = \dfrac{21{,}100}{24.00} = 879$ in.^{3}

Composite section: With $k = 1$ in Eq. (2-3), we find

$K_c = \dfrac{43.20}{43.20 + 60.57} = 0.416$

$\bar{y}_c = (22.99 + 3)0.416 = 10.82$ in.

$I_c = 10.82 \times 25.99 \times 60.57 + 13{,}200 + \dfrac{43.20 \times 6^2}{12}$

$\qquad = 30{,}360$ in.^{4}

$y_{tc} = 22.99 - 10.82 = 12.17$ in.

$S_{tc} = \dfrac{30{,}360}{12.17} = 2{,}495$ in.^{3}

$y_{bc} = 14.41 + 10.82 = 25.23$ in.

$S_{bc} = \dfrac{30{,}360}{25.23} = 1{,}203$ in.^{3}

$y_{cc} = 12.17 + 6 = 18.17$ in.

$S_{cc} = \dfrac{30{,}360}{18.17} = 1{,}671$ in.^{3}

$m = A_c(y_{tc} + e_c) = 43.20(12.17 + 3) = 655.3$ in.^{3}

Stresses [Eqs. (2-3k), (2-3l), and (2-3m)]

	Concrete, f_c, ksi	Steel top flange, f_t, ksi	Steel bottom flange, f_b, ksi
DLs	0	$\dfrac{571 \times 12}{574.2} = 11.93$	$\dfrac{6{,}850}{916} = 7.48$
DLc ($kn = 30$)	$\dfrac{143.6 \times 12}{879 \times 3 \times 10} = 0.07$	$\dfrac{1{,}723}{1{,}172} = 1.47$	$\dfrac{1{,}723}{1{,}088} = 1.58$
LL ($kn = 10$)	$\dfrac{877 \times 12}{1{,}671 \times 10} = 0.63$	$\dfrac{10{,}510}{2{,}495} = 4.21$	$\dfrac{10{,}510}{1{,}203} = 8.74$
	0.70	17.61	17.80

Cover Plate.   Properties of section without cover plate (from Example 4-1):

Composite section with $k = 3$:

$$I_c = 13,810 \text{ in.}^4$$
$$S_{bc} = 599 \text{ in.}^3$$

Composite section with $k = 1$:

$$I_c = 18,700 \text{ in.}^4$$
$$S_{bc} = 662 \text{ in.}^3$$
$$m = 457 \text{ in.}^3$$

The theoretical cover-plate length is determined from Eq. (2-12b), with a, the distance of the maximum-moment section from mid-span, equal to 2.33 ft:

$$L_{cp} = (L - 2a) \sqrt{1 - \frac{S'_{bs}}{S_{bs}}} + 2a$$
$$= (79 - 2 \times 2.33) \sqrt{1 - \frac{502.9}{916}} + 2 \times 2.33 = 54.6 \text{ ft}$$

Allowing about 1 ft extra at each end, the actual length of the cover plate becomes 56 ft 8 in.

The distance from the center of bearing to the theoretical edge of the cover plate is 12.2 ft.   At the plate, the dead-load moment for the steel section alone is

$$M_{Ds} = 0.732 \times \frac{12.2}{2} (79 - 12.2) = 298.3 \text{ kip-ft}$$

The dead-load moment for the composite girder at the edge of the cover plate is

$$M_{Dc} = 0.1841 \times \frac{12.2}{2} (79 - 12.2) = 75.0 \text{ kip-ft}$$

and the live-load moment is

$$M_{LL} = (16 \times 66.8 + 16 \times 52.8 + 4 \times 38.8) \times \frac{1.227}{79} \times 12.2$$
$$= 392 \text{ kip-ft}$$
$$\text{Impact} = \frac{50}{79 + 125} \times 392 = 96 \text{ kip-ft}$$
$$M_{LL} + I = 488 \text{ kip-ft}$$

Thus, the stress in the bottom flange where the cover plate starts is

$$f_b = \frac{298.3 \times 12}{502.9} + \frac{75.0 \times 12}{599} + \frac{488.0 \times 12}{662} = 17.47 \text{ ksi}$$

Shear Connector Spacing (using groups of four studs $\frac{3}{4}$ in. in diameter; see Example 4-1). From Eq. (3-3a), the useful capacity Q_{uc} of one stud is 10.2 kips and of one group,

$$4Q_{uc} = 10.2 \times 4 = 40.8 \text{ kips}$$

The coefficients for computing the factor of safety from Eq. (3-6) are

$$C_{mc} = \frac{M_{Dc}}{M_{LL}} = \frac{143.6}{877} = 0.164$$

$$C_{mi} = \frac{M_{Ds}}{M_{LL}} = \frac{571.1}{877} = 0.652$$

$$C_s = \frac{S_{bc}}{S_{bs}} = \frac{1,203}{916} = 1.313$$

According to Eq. (3-7)

LLFS $= 2.7(1 + C_{mc} + C_{mi}C_s) - (C_{mc} + C_{mi})$
$= 2.7(1 + 0.164 + 0.652 \times 1.313) - (0.164 + 0.652) = 4.64$

At the center line of bearing (no cover plate), with a 16-kip wheel over the bearing, a 16-kip wheel 14 ft away, and a 4-kip wheel 28 ft away:

$$V_{LL} = 16 \times 1.111 + (16 \times 65 + 4 \times 51) \frac{1.227}{79} = 37.1 \text{ kips}$$

$$\text{Impact} = 0.245 \times 37.10 = \underline{ 9.1}$$

$$V_{LL} + \text{impact} = \overline{46.2 \text{ kips}}$$

$$V_{Dc} = 0.1841 \times 79 \times \tfrac{1}{2} = \underline{ 7.3}$$

$$V_c = \overline{53.5 \text{ kips}}$$

$$C_v = \frac{V_{Dc}}{V_{LL} + \text{impact}} = \frac{7.3}{46.2} = 0.16$$

$$\text{FS} = \frac{\text{LLFS} + C_v}{1 + C_v} = \frac{4.64 + 0.16}{1 + 0.16} = 4.14 > 4.0$$

The AASHO specifications (Art. 1.9.5) permit the use of a safety factor of 4 instead of the computed value. In a simply supported beam the formula yields the smallest value of safety factor at the support; since the safety factor already exceeds 4 at the support, the value FS = 4 is used throughout the beam.

At the center line of bearing, the maximum pitch of stud groups is, from Eqs. (3-1) and (3-8),

$$p = \frac{I_c}{mV_c} \frac{4Q_{uc}}{FS} = \frac{18,700}{457 \times 55.5} \times \frac{40.8}{4} = 7.80 \text{ in.}$$

At 7 ft from the center line of bearing (no cover plate):

$$V_{LL} = (16 \times 72 + 16 \times 58 + 4 \times 44)\frac{1.227}{79} = 35.0 \text{ kips}$$

$$\text{Impact} = \frac{50}{72 + 125} \times 35.0 = \quad 8.9$$

$$V_{LL} + \text{impact} = \overline{43.9 \text{ kips}}$$
$$V_{Dc} = 7.3 - 0.1841 \times 7 = \quad 6.0$$
$$V_c = \overline{49.9 \text{ kips}}$$

$$p = \frac{18,700}{457 \times 49.9} \times \frac{40.8}{4.0} = 8.36 \text{ in.}$$

At 14 ft from the center line of bearing (with cover plate):

$$V_{LL} = (16 \times 65 + 16 \times 51 + 4 \times 37)\frac{1.227}{79} = 31.13 \text{ kips}$$

$$\text{Impact} = \frac{50}{63 + 125} \times 31.13 = \quad 8.19$$

$$V_{LL} + \text{impact} = \overline{39.32 \text{ kips}}$$
$$V_{Dc} = 7.27 - 0.1841 \times 14 = \quad 4.69$$
$$V_c = \overline{44.01 \text{ kips}}$$

$$p = \frac{30,360}{655 \times 44.0} \times \frac{40.8}{4.0} = 10.74 \text{ in.}$$

At 21 ft from the center line of bearing (with cover plate):

$$V_{LL} = (16 \times 58 + 16 \times 44 + 4 \times 30)\frac{1.227}{79} = 27.21 \text{ kips}$$

$$\text{Impact} = \frac{50}{58 + 125} \times 27.21 = \quad 7.43$$

$$V_{LL} + \text{impact} = \overline{34.64 \text{ kips}}$$
$$V_{Dc} = 7.27 - 0.1841 \times 21 = \quad 3.40$$
$$V_c = \overline{38.04 \text{ kips}}$$

$$p = \frac{30,360}{655 \times 38.04} \times \frac{40.8}{4.0} = 12.42 \text{ in.}$$

At 28 ft from the center line of bearing (with cover plate):

$$V_{LL} = (16 \times 51 + 16 \times 37 + 4 \times 23)\frac{1.227}{79} = 23.30 \text{ kips}$$

$$\text{Impact} = \frac{50}{51 + 125} \times 23.30 = \underline{6.62}$$

$$V_{LL} + \text{impact} = \underline{29.92 \text{ kips}}$$

$$V_{Dc} = 7.27 - 0.1841 \times 28 = \underline{2.12}$$

$$V_c = \overline{32.04 \text{ kips}}$$

$$p = \frac{30{,}360}{655 \times 32.04} \times \frac{40.8}{4.0} = 14.75 \text{ in.}$$

At 35 ft from the center line of bearing:

$$V_{LL} = (16 \times 44 + 16 \times 30 + 4 \times 16)\frac{1.227}{79} = 19.38 \text{ kips}$$

$$\text{Impact} = \frac{50}{44 + 125} \times 19.38 = \underline{5.73}$$

$$V_{LL} + \text{impact} = \underline{25.11 \text{ kips}}$$

$$V_{Dc} = 7.27 - 0.1841 \times 35 = \underline{0.83}$$

$$V_c = \overline{25.94 \text{ kips}}$$

$$p = \frac{30{,}360}{655 \times 25.94} \times \frac{40.8}{4.0} = 18.22 \text{ in.}$$

Final Section

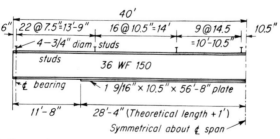

FIG. 4-7. Cover plate and shear-connector spacing for *G2* (Example 4-2).

Dead-load Deflection at Mid-span. If the change of cross section caused by cutting off the tension cover plate is neglected, the dead-load deflection can be computed as follows from Eq. (2-14c):

$$\Delta_{Ds} = \frac{45 \times 0.537 \times 79^4}{2 \times 20 \times 10^3 \times 13{,}200} = 1.23 \text{ in.}$$

$$\Delta_{Dc} = \frac{45 \times 0.1841 \times 79^4}{2 \times 29 \times 10^3 \times 21{,}100} = \underline{0.26}$$

$$\Delta_{Ds} + \Delta_{Dc} = \overline{1.49 \text{ in.}}$$

A computation of deflections taking into account the change in the moment of inertia (exact method) is more complicated and generally gives deflections of 1 per cent to 3 per cent larger than found by the approximate method used above. In this particular case, the exact method gives the dead-load deflection at mid-span as 1.52 in., or 2 per cent in excess of the value found when the change in the moment of inertia is neglected.

Example 4-3.   Simple-span Bridge with Welded Plate Girders, No Shoring (girder $G2$, Fig. 4-1). The welded plate girder in this example has a bottom flange of constant cross section throughout the length of the girder. Should it be desired to reduce the size of the flange to a predetermined smaller plate, the method illustrated in Example 4-2 for determining the cover-plate length may be used to find the point of reduction of the flange size.

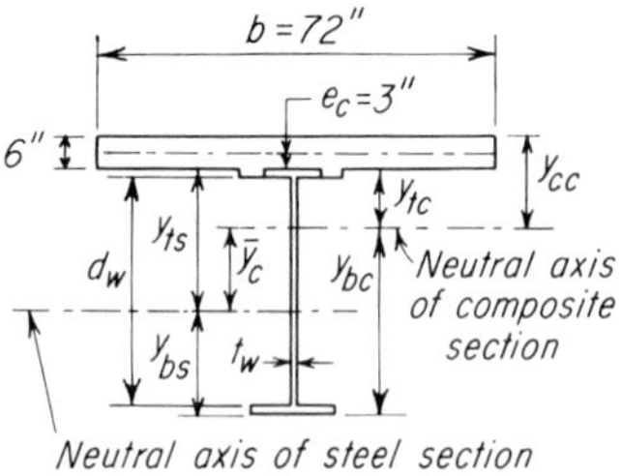

FIG. 4-8. Design section (Example 4-3).

The computation of shrinkage stresses is illustrated for the final cross section. The increase in the top-flange stress is quite large, but the increase in the bottom-flange stress is relatively small. Neither of them exceeds the 25 per cent over-stress permitted by the AASHO specification for Group IV loading. AASHO specifications for design of composite beams do not require computation of shrinkage stresses.

Design Data

Length = 80 ft 0 in.
Distance center to center bearings = 79 ft 0 in.
Live load = H20-S16-44
Live-load distribution to $G2$ = 6.75/5.5 = 1.227
Dead load on steel beam plus its weight (see Example 4-1) = 537.1 + 160.0 = 697.1 lb per ft
Dead load on composite beam (see Example 4-1) = 184.1 lb per ft

Selection of Trial Section. In accordance with the method indicated in Art. 2-13, we compute the maximum bending moments for dead and live loads and the required section modulus for each case:

$$M_{Ds} = \frac{0.697}{8} \times 79^2 = 543.8 \text{ kip-ft}$$

for which the section modulus required is 362.6 in.[3].

$$M_{Dc} = \frac{0.1841}{8} \times 79^2 = 143.6 \text{ kip-ft}$$

and the corresponding section modulus is 95.7 in.[3].

$$M_{LL} = 1,147 \times 1.227 \times \frac{1}{2} = 704 \text{ kip-ft}$$

$$\text{Impact} = \frac{50}{79 + 125} \times 704 = 173 \text{ kip-ft}$$

$$M_{LL} + \text{impact} = 877 \text{ kip-ft}$$

which requires a section modulus of 585 in.[3].

Assume $d_w = 48$ in.; ratio of top-flange area to web area $A_t/A_w = 0.3$, ratio of bottom-flange area to web area $A_b/A_w = 0.8$, $t_w = \frac{3}{8}$ in., $A_w = 18$ in.[2], total area of steel section

$$A_s = 18(1 + 0.3 + 0.8) = 37.80 \text{ in.}^2$$

$$\frac{e_c}{d_w} = \frac{3}{48} = 0.0625$$

$$\frac{S_{ts}}{(A_w + 2A_t)d_w} = 0.331 \qquad \text{(Fig. 5-3)}$$

$k_{Dc} = 3$ $k_{LL} = 1$

$A_c = \dfrac{bt}{kn} = 14.40$ in.[2] (see $A_c = 43.20$ in.[2] (see

        Example 4-1)   Example 4-1)

$K_c = \dfrac{A_c}{A_c + A_s} = \dfrac{14.40}{14.40 + 37.80}$ $K_c = \dfrac{43.20}{43.20 + 37.80}$

$\quad = 0.2759$ $\quad = 0.533$

From Fig. 5-10:

$$\frac{S_{bc}}{(A_w + 2A_b)d_w} = 0.402 \qquad \frac{S_{bc}}{(A_w + 2A_b)d_w} = 0.437$$

$$\frac{(A_w + 2A_t)d_w}{S_{tc}} = 1.15 \qquad \frac{(A_w + 2A_t)d_w}{S_{tc}} = 0.50$$

First Trial Section [with Eqs. (2-11a) and (2-11b), d_w assumed to be 48 in. and A_w 18 in.]

Top flange:

$$A_{Ds} = \frac{362.6}{0.331 \times 48} = \quad 22.82 \text{ in.}^2$$

$$A_{Dc} = \frac{95.7 \times 1.15}{48} = \quad 2.29$$

$$A_{LL} = \frac{584 \times 0.50}{48} = \quad 6.08$$

$$A_w + 2A_t = \quad \overline{31.19 \text{ in.}^2}$$

$$A_w = \quad -18.00$$

$$2A_t = \quad \overline{13.19 \text{ in.}^2}$$

$$A_t = \frac{13.19}{2} = 6.60 \text{ in.}^2$$

$$\frac{A_t}{A_w} = \frac{6.60}{18.00} = 0.367$$

Bottom flange:

$$A_{Ds} = \frac{362.6}{0.331 \times 48} = \quad 22.82 \text{ in.}^2$$

$$A_{Dc} = \frac{95.7}{0.402 \times 48} = \quad 4.96$$

$$A_{LL} = \frac{584}{0.437 \times 48} = \quad 27.84$$

$$A_w + 2A_b = \quad \overline{55.62 \text{ in.}^2}$$

$$A_w = \quad -18.00$$

$$2A_b = \quad \overline{37.62 \text{ in.}^2}$$

$$A_b = \frac{37.62}{2} = 18.81 \text{ in.}^2$$

$$\frac{A_b}{A_w} = \frac{18.81}{18.00} = 1.04$$

$$A_s = 6.60 + 18.81 + 18.00 = 43.41$$

$$\frac{S_{ts}}{(A_w + 2A_t)d_w} = 0.350 \qquad \text{(Fig. 5-3)}$$

$$K_c = \frac{14.40}{14.40 + 43.41} \qquad\qquad\qquad K_c = \frac{43.20}{43.20 + 43.41}$$

$$= 0.2491 \qquad\qquad\qquad\qquad\qquad = 0.499$$

From Fig. 5-11:

$$\frac{S_{bc}}{(A_w + 2A_b)d_w} = 0.413 \qquad\qquad \frac{S_{bc}}{(A_w + 2A_b)d_w} = 0.449$$

$$\frac{(A_w + 2A_t)d_w}{S_{tc}} = 1.14 \qquad\qquad \frac{(A_w + 2A_t)d_w}{S_{tc}} = 0.50$$

Second Trial Section [with Eqs. (2-11a) and (2-11b), d_w assumed to be 48 in. and A_w 18 in.]

Top flange:

$$A_{Ds} = \frac{362.6}{0.350 \times 48} = 21.58 \text{ in.}^2$$

$$A_{Dc} = \frac{95.7 \times 1.14}{48} = 2.27$$

$$A_{LL} = \frac{586 \times 0.50}{48} = 6.08$$

$$A_w + 2A_t = \overline{29.93 \text{ in.}^2}$$

$$A_w = -18.00$$

$$2A_t = \overline{11.93 \text{ in.}^2}$$

$$A_t = \frac{11.93}{2} = 5.96 \text{ in.}^2$$

Try a 12 by ½ top plate; $A_t = 6$ in.^{2}.

Bottom flange:

$$A_{Ds} = \frac{362.6}{0.350 \times 48} = 21.58 \text{ in.}^2$$

$$A_{Dc} = \frac{95.7}{0.413 \times 48} = 4.83$$

$$A_{LL} = \frac{586}{0.449 \times 48} = 27.10$$

$$A_w + 2A_b = \overline{53.51 \text{ in.}^2}$$

$$A_w = -18.00$$

$$2A_b = \overline{35.51 \text{ in.}^2}$$

$$A_b = \frac{35.51}{2} = 17.76 \text{ in.}^2$$

Try a 16 by 1⅛ bottom plate; $A_b = 18.00$ in.^{2}.

Properties of Second Trial Section

Steel section [Eq. (2-2)]; $A_s = 6 + 18 + 18 = 42$ in.^{2}:

$$\bar{y}_s = \frac{(48 + 1.125)18 - (48 + 0.50)6}{2 \times 42} = 7.06 \text{ in.}$$

$$I_s = \frac{1}{4}(48 + 1.125)^2 \times 18 + (48 + 0.50)^2 \times 6 + \frac{1}{12} \times 18$$
$$\times 48^2 - 42 \times 7.06^2 = 15{,}750 \text{ in.}^4$$

$y_{ts} = \frac{1}{2}d + \bar{y}_s + t_t = 24 + 7.06 + 0.50 = 31.56$ in.

$S_{ts} = \dfrac{I_s}{y_{ts}} = 499$ in.^{3}

$y_{bs} = \frac{1}{2}d - \bar{y}_s + t_b = 24 - 7.06 + 1.13 = 18.07$ in.

$S_{bs} = \dfrac{I_s}{y_{bs}} = 872$ in.^{3}

Composite section [Eq. (2-3)] with $k = 3$:

$$K_c = \frac{A_c}{A_c + A_s} = \frac{14.40}{14.40 + 42} = 0.2553$$

$$\bar{y}_c = (y_{ts} + e_c)K_c = (31.56 + 3)0.2553 = 8.82 \text{ in.}$$

$$I_c = (y_{ts} + e_c)\bar{y}_c A_s + I_s + A_c\frac{t^2}{12} = 34.56 \times 8.82 \times 42$$

$$+ \; 15,750 + \frac{14.40 \times 6^2}{12} = 28,600 \text{ in.}^4$$

$y_{tc} = y_{ts} - \bar{y}_c = 31.56 - 8.82 = 22.74$ in.

$S_{tc} = \dfrac{I_c}{y_{tc}} = 1,258$ in.^{3}

$y_{bc} = y_{bs} + \bar{y}_c = 18.07 + 8.82 = 26.89$ in.

$S_{bc} = \dfrac{I_c}{y_{bc}} = 1,064$ in.^{3}

$y_{cc} = y_{tc} + e_c + \dfrac{t}{2} = 22.74 + 3 + 3 = 28.74$ in.

$S_{cc} = \dfrac{I_c}{y_{cc}} = 995$ in.^{3}

Composite section [Eq. (2-3)] with $k = 1$:

$$K_c = \frac{43.20}{43.20 + 42} = 0.507$$

$$\bar{y}_c = (31.56 + 3)0.507 = 17.52 \text{ in.}$$

$$I_c = 34.56 \times 17.52 \times 42 + 15,750 + \frac{43.20 \times 6^2}{12} = 41,300 \text{ in.}^4$$

$y_{tc} = 31.56 - 17.52 = 14.04$ in.
$S_{tc} = 2,942$ in.^{3}
$y_{bc} = 18.07 + 17.52 = 35.59$ in.
$S_{bc} = 1,161$ in.^{3}
$y_{cc} = 14.04 + 6 = 20.04$ in.
$S_{cc} = 2,061$ in.^{3}
$m = A_c(y_{tc} + e_c) = 43.20(14.04 + 3) = 736$ in.^{3}

Stresses

	Concrete, f_c, ksi	Steel top flange, f_t, ksi	Steel bottom flange, f_b, ksi
DLs	0	$\dfrac{543.8 \times 12}{499} = 13.08$	$\dfrac{6,530}{872} = 7.49$
DLc $(kn = 30)$	$\dfrac{143.6 \times 12}{995 \times 30} = 0.06$	$\dfrac{1,723}{1,258} = 1.37$	$\dfrac{1,723}{1,064} = 1.62$
LL $(kn = 10)$	$\dfrac{877 \times 12}{2,061 \times 10} = 0.51$	$\dfrac{10,560}{2,942} = 3.57$	$\dfrac{10,560}{1,161} = 9.05$
	$\overline{0.57}$	$\overline{18.02}$	$\overline{18.16}$

Shrinkage Stresses [from Eqs. (2-4a) and (2-4b), with $k = 1$ and $E_s = 29 \times 10^3$ ksi]

	Top flange, ksi	Bottom flange, ksi
Load stresses..............................	18.02	18.16
$0.0002 \times 29 \times 10^3 \left(0.507 + \dfrac{(20.04 - 3)43.2}{2,942} \right)$	4.39	
$0.0002 \times 29 \times 10^3 \left(-0.507 + \dfrac{17.04 \times 43.2}{1,161} \right)$	.....	0.74
	$\overline{22.41}$	$\overline{18.90}$

Allowable stress (with shrinkage) = $1.25 \times 18 = 22.50$ ksi

Shear Connector Spacing (using groups of four studs $\frac{3}{4}$ in. in diameter; see Example 4-1). According to Eq. (3-3a), the useful capacity of one stud is 10.2 kips and of one group

$$4Q_{uc} = 10.2 \times 4 = 40.8 \text{ kips}$$

Next, the factor of safety is needed. The components are

$$C_{mc} = \frac{M_{Dc}}{M_{LL}} = \frac{143.6}{877} = 0.164$$

$$C_{mi} = \frac{M_{Ds}}{M_{LL}} = \frac{543.8}{877} = 0.621$$

$$C_s = \frac{S_{bc}}{S_{bs}} = \frac{1,161}{872} = 1.332$$

Substituting in Eq. (3-7), we find

$$LLFS = 2.7(1 + C_{mc} + C_{mi}C_s) - (C_{mc} + C_{mi}) = 2.7(1 + 0.164$$
$$+ 0.621 \times 1.332) - (0.164 + 0.621) = 4.59$$

At the center line of bearing (values of V_{LL}, V_{Dc}, V_c, and C_v are the same as in Example 4-2 at all cross sections): $V_{LL} = 37.10$ kips, impact $= 9.1$ kips, $V_{Dc} = 7.3$ kips, $V_c = 53.5$ kips, and

$$C_v = \frac{V_{Dc}}{V_{LL} + \text{impact}} = 0.16$$

According to Eq. (3-6)

$$FS = \frac{4.59 + 0.16}{1 + 0.16} = 4.09 > 4$$

So FS = 4 is used at all cross sections.
Applying Eq. (3-8), we find the pitch:

$$p = \frac{I_c}{mV_c} \frac{4Q_{uc}}{FS} = \frac{41,300}{736 \times 53.5} \times \frac{40.8}{4} = 10.71 \text{ in.}$$

At 7 ft from the center line of bearing:

$$V_{LL} = 35.0 \text{ kips}$$
$$\text{Impact} = \underline{\quad 8.9 \quad}$$
$$V_{LL} + \text{impact} = 43.9 \text{ kips}$$
$$V_{Dc} = \underline{\quad 6.0 \quad}$$
$$V_c = 49.9 \text{ kips}$$
$$p = \frac{53.5}{49.9} \times 10.71 = 11.47 \text{ in.}$$

At 14 ft from the center line of bearing:

$$V_{LL} = 31.13 \text{ kips}$$
$$\text{Impact} = \underline{\quad 8.19 \quad}$$
$$V_{LL} + \text{impact} = 39.32 \text{ kips}$$
$$V_{Dc} = \underline{\quad 4.69 \quad}$$
$$V_c = 44.01 \text{ kips}$$
$$p = \frac{53.5}{44.01} \times 10.71 = 13.01 \text{ in.}$$

At 21 ft from the center line of bearing:

$$V_{LL} = 27.21 \text{ kips}$$
$$\text{Impact} = 7.43$$
$$V_{LL} + \text{impact} = 34.64 \text{ kips}$$
$$V_{Dc} = 3.40$$
$$V_c = 38.04 \text{ kips}$$
$$p = \frac{53.5}{38.04} \times 10.71 = 15.05 \text{ in.}$$

At 28 ft from the center line of bearing:

$$V_{LL} = 23.30 \text{ kips}$$
$$\text{Impact} = 6.62$$
$$V_{LL} + \text{impact} = 29.92 \text{ kips}$$
$$V_{Dc} = 2.12$$
$$V_c = 32.04 \text{ kips}$$
$$p = \frac{53.5}{32.04} \times 10.71 = 17.87 \text{ in.}$$

At 35 ft from the center line of bearing:

$$V_{LL} = 19.38 \text{ kips}$$
$$\text{Impact} = 5.73$$
$$V_{LL} + \text{impact} = 25.11 \text{ kips}$$
$$V_{Dc} = 0.83$$
$$V_c = 25.94 \text{ kips}$$
$$p = \frac{53.5}{25.94} \times 10.71 = 22.07 \text{ in.}$$

Final Section

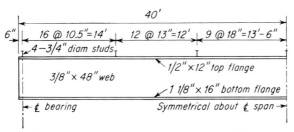

FIG. 4-9. Shear-connector spacing on plate girder (Example 4-3).

Example 4-4. Simple-span Bridge with Rolled Beams, Cover Plates, and Shoring (girder $G2$, Fig. 4-1). When a composite beam is supported temporarily at intermediate points during the casting and curing of the slab, the noncomposite dead load is carried by the steel section, which acts as a continuous beam. Additional stresses are induced by removal of the temporary supports, but these are resisted by the composite section. If three or more intermediate supports are used, the sum of the stresses from the two loading conditions is nearly the same as stresses computed from the assumption that the dead load is carried by the composite section and that no additional stresses are induced by shore removal.[1] This second simpler method is followed in Example 4-4.

The assumption that dead load is carried by the composite section also gives reasonably accurate loads for the design of shear connectors if three or more intermediate supports are used during the construction. It is assumed in the example that this condition is fulfilled.

Live-load deflections were computed by one rigorous and one approximate method—on the basis of actual variable moment of inertia and on the assumption that the larger moment of inertia is constant throughout the span. The difference in the deflections obtained by the two methods is negligible; therefore only calculations by the simpler approximate method are shown.

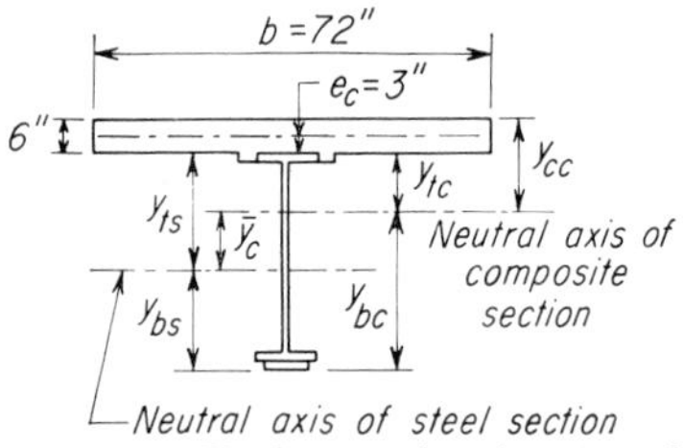

Fig. 4-10. Design section for shored beam (Example 4-4).

Design Data

Length = 80 ft 0 in.

Distance center to center bearings = 79 ft 0 in.

Live load = H20-S16-44

Live-load distribution to $G2$ = 1.227

Dead load on composite beam (see Example 4-1) = 537.1 + 184.1 + 180.0 = 901.2 lb per ft

Selection of Trial Section. As discussed in Art. 2-12, we first find the maximum bending moments for dead and live loads and

---

[1] This method of computation is based on the assumption that the beam is supported temporarily at every point of its length.

the section modulus for each case:

$$M_{Dc} = \frac{0.901}{8} \times 79^2 = 703 \text{ kip-ft}$$

for which the section modulus required is 469 in.^{3}

$$M_{LL} = 1{,}147 \times \tfrac{1}{2} \times 1.227 = 704 \text{ kip-ft}$$

$$\text{Impact} = \frac{50}{79 \times 125} \times 704 = 176 \text{ kip-ft}$$

$$M_{LL} + \text{impact} = 877 \text{ kip-ft}$$

requiring a section modulus of 585 in.^{3}

Assume a 36 WF 150, with area $A_s = 44.16$ in.^{2}, depth $d = 35.84$ in., moment of inertia $I_s = 9{,}012$ in.^{4}, and section modulus $S_s = 502.9$ in.^{3}. The following values are computed as in Examples 4-1 and 4-2:

$$\frac{e_c}{d} = 0.0837$$

$$k_{Dc} = 3 \qquad\qquad k_{LL} = 1$$
$$A_c = 14.40 \text{ in.}^2 \qquad A_c = 43.20 \text{ in.}^2$$
$$K_c = 0.246 \qquad\qquad K_c = 0.495$$

From Fig. 5-1 and 5-2 for $k = 3$ and 1, respectively,

$$\frac{S_{bc}}{A_s d} = 0.388 \qquad\qquad \frac{S_{bc}}{A_s d} = 0.425$$

$$\frac{A_s d}{S_{tc}} = 1.435 \qquad\qquad \frac{A_s d}{S_{tc}} = 0.635$$

Substituting in Eq. (2-8b), we find the area requirements of the steel section to be

Top flange:

$$A_{Dc} = \frac{469 \times 1.435}{35.84} = 18.77 \text{ in.}^2$$

$$A_{LL} = \frac{585 \times 0.635}{35.84} = 10.35$$

$$\text{Required } A_B = \overline{29.12 \text{ in.}^2}$$

Bottom flange:

$$A_{Dc} = \frac{469}{35.84 \times 0.388} = 33.70 \text{ in.}^2$$

$$A_{LL} = \frac{585}{35.84 \times 0.425} = 38.35$$

$$\text{Required } A_s = \overline{72.05 \text{ in.}^2}$$

Try a 36 WF 150, with area $A_B = 44.16$ in.^{2}.

Then the required area of the cover plate A_p is

$$\tfrac{1}{2}(72.05 - 44.16) = 13.95 \text{ in.}^2$$

Try a $1\tfrac{1}{4}$ by $10\tfrac{1}{2}$ plate, $A_p = 13.13$ in.^{2}.

Properties of Trial Section

Steel section (see Eq. 2-1):

$$K_s = \frac{A_p}{A_s} = \frac{A_p}{A_p + A_B} = \frac{13.13}{13.13 + 44.16} = 0.2291$$

$\bar{y}_s = \tfrac{1}{2}(d + t_p)K_s = \tfrac{1}{2}(35.84 + 1.25)0.2291 = 4.25$ in.

$I_s = \tfrac{1}{2}(d + t_p)\bar{y}_s A_B + I_B = 18.55 \times 4.25 \times 44.16 + 9{,}012$
$\quad = 12{,}490$ in.^{4}

$$y_{ts} = \frac{d}{2} + \bar{y}_s = 17.92 + 4.25 = 22.17 \text{ in.}$$

$$S_{ts} = \frac{I_s}{y_{ts}} = 563 \text{ in.}^3$$

$$y_{bs} = \frac{d}{2} + t_p - \bar{y}_s = 17.92 + 1.25 - 4.25 = 14.92 \text{ in.}$$

$$S_{bs} = \frac{I_s}{y_{bs}} = 837 \text{ in.}^3$$

Composite section: With $k = 3$ and using Eq. (2-3), we compute

$$K_c = \frac{A_c}{A_c + A_s} = \frac{14.40}{14.40 + 57.29} = 0.2008$$

$\bar{y}_c = (y_{ts} + 3)K_c = (22.17 + 3)0.2008 = 5.05$ in.

$I_c = \bar{y}_c(y_{ts} + e_c)A_s + I_s + A_c\dfrac{t^2}{12} = 5.05 \times 25.17 \times 57.29$

$$+ 12{,}490 + \frac{14.40 \times 6^2}{12} = 19{,}820 \text{ in.}^4$$

$y_{tc} = y_{ts} - \bar{y}_c = 22.17 - 5.05 = 17.12$ in.

$S_{tc} = \dfrac{19{,}820}{17.12} = 1{,}158$ in.^{3}

$y_{bc} = y_{bs} + \bar{y}_c = 14.92 + 5.05 = 19.97$ in.

$S_{bc} = \dfrac{19{,}820}{19.97} = 993$ in.^{3}

$y_{cc} = y_{tc} + e_c + \dfrac{t}{2} = 17.12 + 3 + 3 = 23.12$ in.

$S_{cc} = \dfrac{19{,}820}{23.12} = 857$ in.^{3}

Composite section with $k = 1$:

$$K_c = \frac{43.20}{43.20 + 57.29} = 0.430$$

$$\bar{y}_c = (22.17 + 3)0.430 = 10.82 \text{ in.}$$

$$I_c = 10.82 \times 25.17 \times 57.29 + 12,490 + \frac{43.20 \times 6^2}{12}$$

$$= 28,220 \text{ in.}^4$$

$$y_{tc} = 22.17 - 10.82 = 11.35 \text{ in.}$$

$$S_{tc} = \frac{28,220}{11.35} = 2,486 \text{ in.}^3$$

$$y_{bc} = 14.92 + 10.82 = 25.74 \text{ in.}$$

$$S_{bc} = \frac{28,220}{25.74} = 1,096 \text{ in.}^3$$

$$y_{cc} = 11.35 + 6 = 17.35 \text{ in.}$$

$$S_{cc} = \frac{28,220}{17.35} = 1,627 \text{ in.}^3$$

$$m = A_c(y_{tc} + e_c) = 43.20(11.35 + 3) = 620 \text{ in.}^3$$

Stresses [Eqs. (2-3k), (2-3l), and (2-3m)]

	Concrete, f_c, ksi	Steel top flange, f_t, ksi	Steel bottom flange, f_b, ksi
DLc ($kn = 30$)	$\dfrac{703.0 \times 12}{857 \times 30} = 0.33$	$\dfrac{8,440}{1,158} = 7.28$	$\dfrac{8,440}{993} = 8.50$
LL ($kn = 10$)	$\dfrac{877 \times 12}{1,627 \times 10} = 0.65$	$\dfrac{10,560}{2,486} = 4.23$	$\dfrac{10,560}{1,096} = 9.59$
	$\overline{0.98}$	$\overline{11.51}$	$\overline{18.09}$

Cover Plate

Properties of section without cover plate (from Example 4-1): Composite section with $k = 3$:

$$S_{bc} = 599 \text{ in.}^3$$

Composite section with $k = 1$:

$$I_c = 18,700 \text{ in.}^4$$
$$S_{bc} = 662 \text{ in.}^3$$
$$m = 457 \text{ in.}^3$$

The theoretical cover-plate length is determined from Eq. (2-12c), with a, the distance of the maximum-moment section from mid-span, equal to 2.33 ft:

$$L_{cp} = (L - 2a) \sqrt{\frac{1 - S_{bc}}{S_{bc}}} + 2a = (79 - 2 \times 2.33) \sqrt{1 - \frac{599}{993}}$$
$$+ 2 \times 2.33 = 51.5 \text{ ft}$$

Allowing 1 ft additional at each end the actual length of the cover plate becomes 53.5 ft.

The distance from the theoretical edge of the cover plate to the center of bearing is 13.75 ft. At the plate, the dead-load moment for the composite beam is

$$M_{Dc} = 0.901 \times \frac{13.75}{2} (79 - 13.75) = 404 \text{ kip-ft}$$

and the live-load moment is

$$M_{LL} = (16 \times 65.25 + 16 \times 51.25 + 4 \times 37.25)$$
$$\times \frac{1.227}{79} \times 13.75 = 30 \text{ kip-ft}$$
$$\text{Impact} = 0.245 \times 430 = 105$$
$$M_{LL} + \text{impact} = \overline{535 \text{ kip-ft}}$$

Then the stress in the bottom flange at the section where the cover plate starts is

$$f_b = \frac{404 \times 12}{599} + \frac{535 \times 12}{662} = 17.81 \text{ ksi}$$

Shear Connector Spacing (using groups of four studs $\frac{3}{4}$ in. in diameter; see Example 4-1). From Eq. (3-3a), the useful capacity Q_{uc} of one stud is 10.2 kips and of one group

$$4Q_{uc} = 10.2 \times 4 = 40.8 \text{ kips}$$

The coefficients for computing the safety factor from Eq. (3-6) are

$$C_{mc} = \frac{M_{Dc}}{M_{LL}} = \frac{703}{877} = 0.802$$
$$C_{mi} = \frac{M_{Ds}}{M_{LL}} = \frac{0}{877} = 0$$
$$C_s = \frac{S_{bc}}{S_{bs}} = \frac{1,096}{837} = 1.309$$

According to Eq. (3-7)

$$LLFS = 2.7(1 + C_{mc} + C_{mi}C_s) - (C_{mc} + C_{mi})$$
$$= 2.7(1 + 0.802 + 0 \times 1.309) - (0.802 + 0) = 4.06$$

In the following computations, values of V_{LL} and impact are the same as in Example 4-2.

At the center line of bearing:

$$V_{LL} = 37.1 \text{ kips}$$
$$\text{Impact} = \underline{9.1}$$
$$V_{LL} + \text{impact} = \underline{46.2 \text{ kips}}$$
$$V_{Dc} = 0.901 \times 79 \times \tfrac{1}{2} = \underline{35.6}$$
$$V_c = 81.8 \text{ kips}$$

$$C_v = \frac{V_{Dc}}{V_{LL} + \text{impact}} = \frac{35.6}{46.2} = 0.77$$

$$FS = \frac{LLFS + C_v}{1 + C_v} = \frac{4.06 + 0.77}{1 + 0.77} = 2.73$$

$$p = \frac{I_c}{mV_c} \frac{4Q_{uc}}{FS} = \frac{18,700}{457 \times 81.8} \times \frac{40.8}{2.73} = 7.48 \text{ in.}$$

At 7 ft from the center line of bearing:

$$V_{LL} = 35.0 \text{ kips}$$
$$\text{Impact} = \underline{8.9}$$
$$V_{LL} + \text{impact} = \underline{43.9 \text{ kips}}$$
$$V_{Dc} = 35.6 - 0.901 \times 7 = \underline{29.3}$$
$$V_c = 73.2 \text{ kips}$$

$$C_v = \frac{29.3}{43.9} = 0.67$$

$$FS = \frac{4.06 + 0.67}{1 + 0.67} = 2.83$$

$$p = \frac{18,700}{457 \times 73.2} \times \frac{40.8}{2.83} = 8.06 \text{ in.}$$

At 14 ft from the center line of bearing:

$$V_{LL} = 31.1 \text{ kips}$$
$$\text{Impact} = \underline{8.2}$$
$$V_{LL} + \text{impact} = \underline{39.3 \text{ kips}}$$
$$V_{Dc} = 35.6 - 0.901 \times 14 = \underline{23.0}$$
$$V_c = 62.3 \text{ kips}$$

$$C_v = \frac{23.0}{39.3} = 0.58$$

$$FS = \frac{4.06 + 0.58}{1 + 0.58} = 2.94$$

$$p = \frac{28,220}{620 \times 62.3} \times \frac{40.8}{2.94} = 10.14 \text{ in.}$$

At 21 ft from the center line of bearing:

$$V_{LL} = 27.2 \text{ kips}$$
$$\text{Impact} = 7.4$$
$$V_{LL} + \text{impact} = \overline{34.6 \text{ kips}}$$
$$V_{Dc} = 35.6 - 0.901 \times 21 = 16.7$$
$$V_c = \overline{51.3 \text{ kips}}$$

$$C_v = \frac{16.7}{34.6} = 0.48$$

$$FS = \frac{4.06 + 0.48}{1 + 0.48} = 3.07$$

$$p = \frac{28,220}{620 \times 51.3} \times \frac{40.8}{3.07} = 11.79 \text{ in.}$$

At 28 ft from the center line of bearing:

$$V_{LL} = 23.3 \text{ kips}$$
$$\text{Impact} = 6.6$$
$$V_{LL} + \text{impact} = \overline{29.9 \text{ kips}}$$
$$V_{Dc} = 35.6 - 0.901 \times 28 = 10.4$$
$$V_c = \overline{40.3 \text{ kips}}$$

$$C_v = \frac{10.4}{29.9} = 0.35$$

$$FS = \frac{4.06 + 0.35}{1 + 0.35} = 3.27$$

$$p = \frac{28,220}{620 \times 40.3} \times \frac{40.8}{3.27} = 14.10 \text{ in.}$$

At 35 ft from the center line of bearing:

$$V_{LL} = 19.4 \text{ kips}$$
$$\text{Impact} = 5.7$$
$$V_{LL} + \text{impact} = \overline{25.1 \text{ kips}}$$
$$V_{Dc} = 35.6 - 0.901 \times 35 = 4.1$$
$$V_c = \overline{29.2 \text{ kips}}$$

$$C_v = \frac{4.1}{25.1} = 0.16$$

$$\text{FS} = \frac{4.06 + 0.16}{1 + 0.16} = 3.64$$

$$p = \frac{28{,}220}{620 \times 29.2} \times \frac{40.8}{3.64} = 17.50 \text{ in.}$$

Final Section

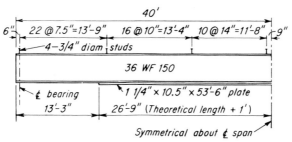

FIG. 4-11. Cover plate and shear-connector spacing for shored beam (Example 4-4).

Live-load Deflections. Assuming that the maximum live-load deflection occurs at mid-span with the loads in position for maximum design moment and neglecting the change of cross section caused by cutting off the tension cover plate, the deflection can be computed as follows from Eq. (2-15a), with $k = 1$ and $P_T = 4 \times 1.227 \times 1.245 = 6.11$ kips.

$$\Delta = \frac{324}{E_s I_c} P_T (L^3 - 555L + 4{,}780)$$

$$= \frac{324 \times 6.11}{29 \times 10^3 \times 28{,}220} (79^3 - 555 \times 79 + 4{,}780) = 1.09 \text{ in.}$$

The allowable deflection is $\frac{1}{800}$ of the span length, or 1.19 in.

For the loads in the same position as described above, deflection computations taking into account the change of the cross section give deflection at mid-span of 1.10 in. This method requires tedious calculations. In view of the small difference from the approximate method illustrated above, it is not recommended except in unusual cases.

Example 4-5. Three-span Continuous Bridge with Rolled Beams and Cover Plates, No Shoring (girder $G2$, Fig. 4-1). The three-span continous bridge in this example is designed for composite action in the positive-moment regions between the dead-load points of contraflexure. The negative moments are resisted by the steel beam with symmetrical cover plates on top and bottom flanges.

The moment and shear curves of this example were calculated from influence lines of a similar continuous unit which had a slightly different typical cross section and thus different ratios of dead loads to live loads. After the beam sections from these curves have been selected, the relative elastic properties of the resulting beam should be compared with the relative elastic properties of the beam for which the influence lines were calculated, and if the variations are small, then no further moment calculations are necessary. However, if the variations are large, it will be necessary to calculate a new set of moment curves for the new beam. For simplicity, it is assumed in this example that the variations are small and no further moment calculations are necessary.

Usually the variations in the shear curves for the preliminary section and the final section will be small, and a second set of shear curves need not be calculated. Thus, shear connector spacing can be calculated from the initial shear curves, and final drawings can be made while final sections are being selected.

Welded field splices are located at points 5.5 and 10.5 (see Fig. 4-13), which nearly coincide with the dead-load points of contraflexure. The moment curves in Fig. 4-12 show that alternating stress will occur at these points. To satisfy the design requirements for alternating stress, AASHO specifications Art. 1.6.5, the design moment must be taken as the sum of the numerically larger moment and 50 per cent of the numerically smaller moment. Since this condition may govern the size of the minimum cross section, a check must be made at these locations. The moments at point 5.5 are somewhat larger than at point 10.5; therefore, the check is made only at point 5.5.

The live-load factor of safety for the design of shear connectors is determined at two points of maximum positive moment and at the maximum negative-moment section. The smallest value is used in the design.

Design Data

Spans: two 80-ft 6-in. end spans and one 100-ft intermediate span

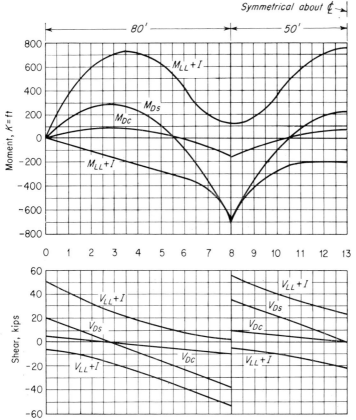

FIG. 4-12. Moment and shear curves for three-span continuous beam (Example 4-5).

Distances center to center bearings: 80-ft end spans, 100-ft intermediate span

Live load = H20-S16-44

Live-load distribution = 1.227

Dead load on steel beam alone (see Example 4-1) = 537.1 + 195.0 = 732.1 lb per ft

Dead load on composite section (see Example 4-1) = 184.1 lb per ft

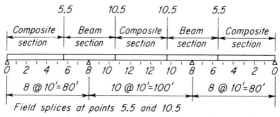

Field splices at points 5.5 and 10.5

FIG. 4-13. Location of field splices in three-span continuous beam (Example 4-5).

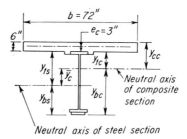

FIG. 4-14. Design section (Example 4-5).

Rolled Beam Section.   Check field splice at point 5.5 for minimum beam section.

From Fig. 4-12:

$$+(M_{LL} + I) = +530 \text{ kip-ft} \qquad -(M_{LL} + I) = -304 \text{ kip-ft}$$

$$M_{Ds} = + 30 \qquad\qquad M_{Ds} = + 30$$

$$M_{Dc} = + 20 \qquad\qquad M_{Dc} = + 20$$

$$\text{Max} + M = +\overline{580 \text{ kip-ft}} \qquad \text{Max} - M = -\overline{254 \text{ kip-ft}}$$

Design M = 580 kip-ft + ½ × 254 kip-ft = 707 kip-ft

Required section modulus (welded splice) 707 × $^{12}\!\!/_{18}$ = 471 in.³
    Assume a 36 WF 150, with area A_s = 44.16 in.², depth d = 35.84 in., I_s = 9,012 in.⁴, and S_s = 502.9 in.³ (the following values are taken from Example 4-1).

$$\frac{e_c}{d} = 0.084 \qquad\qquad \frac{S_s}{A_s} = 11.39 \text{ in.}$$

$$k_{Dc} = 3 \qquad\qquad k_{LL} = 1$$

$$A_c = 14.40 \text{ in.}^2 \qquad A_c = 43.20 \text{ in.}^2$$

$$K_c = 0.2459 \qquad\qquad K_c = 0.495$$

From Figs. 5-1 and 5-2 for $k = 3$ and 1, respectively:

$$\frac{S_{bc}}{A_s d} = 0.388 \qquad \frac{S_{bc}}{A_s d} = 0.425$$

$$\frac{A_s d}{S_{tc}} = 1.435 \qquad \frac{A_s d}{S_{tc}} = 0.635$$

Positive-moment Sections in End Spans

Point 3:

	Moments, kip-ft	Required section modulus, in.³
$M_{Ds} =$	287	191
$M_{Dc} =$	80	53
$M_{LL} + I =$	710	473

Substituting in Eqs. (2-7) and (2-8):

Top flange:

$$A_{Ds} = \frac{M_{Ds}}{f_t}\frac{A_s}{S_s} = \frac{191}{11.39} \qquad\qquad = 16.77 \text{ in.}^2$$

$$A_{Dc} = \frac{M_{Dc}}{f_t}\frac{A_s d}{S_{tc}}\frac{1}{d} = \frac{53 \times 1.435}{35.84} = 2.12$$

$$A_{LL} = \frac{M_{LL}}{f_t}\frac{A_s d}{S_{tc}}\frac{1}{d} = \frac{473 \times 0.635}{35.84} = 8.38$$

$$A_B = \overline{27.27 \text{ in.}^2}$$

Bottom flange:

$$A_{Ds} = \frac{M_{Ds}}{f_b}\frac{A_s}{S_s} = \frac{191}{11.39} \qquad\qquad = 16.77 \text{ in.}^2$$

$$A_{Dc} = \frac{M_{Dc}}{f_b}\frac{A_s d}{S_{bc}}\frac{1}{d} = \frac{53}{35.84 \times 0.388} = 3.81$$

$$A_{LL} = \frac{M_{LL}}{f_b}\frac{A_s d}{S_{bc}}\frac{1}{d} = \frac{473}{35.84 \times 0.425} = 31.06$$

$$A_s = \overline{51.64 \text{ in.}^2}$$

Try a 36 WF 150: $A_B = 44.16$ in.²

$$\text{Area 36 WF 150} = \overline{44.16} \text{ in.}^2$$

$$2A_p = \overline{7.48} \text{ in.}^2$$

$$\text{Required } A_p = 3.74$$

Point 3.5:

	Moments, kip-ft	Required section modulus, in.³
$M_{Ds} =$	270	180
$M_{Dc} =$	78	52
$M_{LL} + I =$	730	487

$$A_{Ds} = \frac{180}{11.39} \qquad = \quad 15.80 \text{ in.}^2$$

$$A_{Dc} = \frac{52}{35.84 \times 0.388} = \quad 3.74$$

$$A_{LL} = \frac{487}{35.84 \times 0.425} \quad = \quad 31.98$$

$$\overline{51.52 \text{ in.}^2}$$

$$A_B = \frac{-44.16}{7.36 \text{ in.}^2}$$

$$\text{Required } A_p = \frac{7.36}{2} = 3.68 \text{ in.}^2$$

Try $\frac{7}{16}$ by 8 plate: $A_p = 3.50$ in.^{2}.

$$A_s = A_p + A_B = 3.50 + 44.16 = 47.66$$

Properties of Trial Section

Steel section [from Eq. (2-1)]:

$$K_s = \frac{3.50}{3.50 + 44.16} = 0.0734$$

$\bar{y}_s = \frac{1}{2}(35.84 + 0.44)0.0734 = 1.35$ in.

$I_s = 1.33 \times 18.14 \times 44.16 + 9{,}012 = 10{,}080$ in.^{4}

$y_{ts} = 17.92 + 1.33 = 19.25$ in.

$S_{ts} = 524$ in.^{3}

$y_{bs} = 17.92 - 1.33 + 0.44 = 17.03$ in.

$S_{bs} = 592$ in.^{3}

Composite section [from (Eq. 2-3)] with $k = 3$:

$$K_c = \frac{14.40}{14.40 + 47.66} = 0.232$$

$\bar{y}_c = (19.25 + 3)0.232 = 5.16$ in.

$$I_c = 5.16 \times 22.25 \times 47.66 + 10{,}080 + \frac{14.40 \times 6^2}{12}$$

$\qquad = 15{,}600$ in.^{4}

$y_{tc} = 19.25 - 5.16 = 14.09$ in.

$S_{tc} = 1{,}107$ in.^{3}

$y_{bc} = 17.03 + 5.16 = 22.19$ in.

$S_{bc} = 703$ in.^{3}

$y_{cc} = 19.25 - 5.16 + 6.00 = 20.09$ in.

$S_{cc} = 777$ in.^{3}

Composite section with $k = 1$:

$$K_c = \frac{43.20}{43.20 + 47.66} = 0.475$$

$\bar{y}_c = (19.25 + 3)0.475 = 10.58$ in.

$$I_c = 10.58 \times 22.25 \times 47.66 + 10,080 + \frac{43.20 \times 6^2}{12}$$

$ = 21,430$ in.^{4}

$y_{tc} = 19.25 - 10.58 = 8.67$ in.

$S_{tc} = 2,472$ in.^{3}

$y_{bc} = 17.03 + 10.58 = 27.61$ in.

$S_{bc} = 776$ in.^{3}

$y_{cc} = 19.25 - 10.58 + 6 = 14.67$ in.

$S_{cc} = 1,461$ in.^{3}

$m = 43.20(8.67 + 3) = 504$ in.^{3}

Stresses

	f_c, ksi	f_t, ksi	f_b, ksi
DLs	0	$\dfrac{287 \times 12}{524} = 6.58$	$\dfrac{3,444}{592} = 5.82$
DLc	$\dfrac{80 \times 12}{777 \times 30} = 0.04$	$\dfrac{960}{1,107} = 0.87$	$\dfrac{960}{703} = 1.37$
LL	$\dfrac{710 \times 12}{1,461 \times 10} = 0.58$	$\dfrac{8,520}{2,472} = 3.45$	$\dfrac{8,520}{776} = 10.98$
	$\overline{0.62}$	$\overline{10.90}$	$\overline{18.17}$

Properties of Section without Cover Plate (from Example 4-1)

Composite section with $k = 3$:

$$I_c = 13,810 \text{ in.}^4$$
$$S_{bc} = 599 \text{ in.}^3$$

Composite section with $k = 1$:

$$I_c = 18,700 \text{ in.}^4$$
$$S_{bc} = 662 \text{ in.}^3$$
$$m = 457 \text{ in.}^3$$

Stress calculations indicate that a cover plate is not needed at these points:

Point 1.9:

$$f_b = \frac{255 \times 12}{502.9} + \frac{75 \times 12}{599} + \frac{580 \times 12}{662} = 18.11 \text{ ksi}$$

Point 4.5:

$$f_b = \frac{185 \times 12}{502.9} + \frac{55 \times 12}{599} + \frac{685 \times 12}{662} = 17.93 \text{ ksi}$$

Negative-moment Sections

Point 8:

$$\begin{aligned} M_{Ds} &= 675 \text{ kip-ft} \\ M_{Dc} &= 160 \\ M_{LL} + I &= 650 \\ \hline M &= 1{,}485 \text{ kip-ft} \end{aligned}$$

Area of cover plates from Eq. (2-13a) (assume $t_p = 1.0$ in.):

$$A_p = \frac{1{,}485 \times {}^{12}\!/_{18}(35.84 + 2.0) - 2 \times 9{,}012}{(35.84 + 1.0)^2} = 14.33 \text{ in.}^2$$

Try $10\tfrac{1}{2}$ by $1\tfrac{3}{8}$ plate: $A_p = 14.44$ in.^{2}.

$$I_s = 9{,}012 + 14.44(35.84 + 1.375)^2 \times \tfrac{1}{2} = 19{,}010 \text{ in.}^4$$

$$f_t = f_b = \frac{1{,}485 \times 12(17.92 + 1.375)}{19{,}010} = 18.09 \text{ ksi}$$

Cover plate is not needed where the moment drops below $M_B = 502.9 \times {}^{18}\!/_{12} = 754$ kip-ft (resisting design moment of a 36 WF 150 steel beam). Thus, a cover plate is not needed at these points:

Point 6.8:

$$\begin{aligned} M_{Ds} &= 280 \text{ kip-ft} \\ M_{Dc} &= 60 \\ M_{LL} &= 395 \\ \hline &\ 735 \text{ kip-ft} \end{aligned}$$

$$f = 18 \times {}^{735}\!/_{754} = 17.55 \text{ ksi}$$

Point 9.2:

$$\begin{aligned} M_{Ds} &= 295 \text{ kip-ft} \\ M_{Dc} &= 65 \\ M_{LL} &= 380 \\ \hline &\ 740 \text{ kip-ft} \end{aligned}$$

$$f = 18 \times {}^{740}\!/_{754} = 17.67 \text{ ksi}$$

Positive-moment Sections—Center Span

Point 13:

Moments, kip-ft	Required section modulus, in.³
$M_{Ds} = 225$	150
$M_{Dc} = 70$	47
$M_{LL} + I = 750$	500

Bottom flange:

$$A_{Ds} = \frac{150}{11.39} = 13.17 \text{ in.}^2$$

$$A_{Dc} = \frac{47}{35.84 \times 0.388} = 3.38$$

$$A_{LL} = \frac{500}{35.84 \times 0.425} = 32.83$$

$$\overline{49.38 \text{ in.}^2}$$

$$A_B = -44.16$$

$$\overline{5.22 \text{ in.}^2}$$

$$\text{Required } A_p = \frac{5.22}{2} = 2.61 \text{ in.}^2$$

Try $\frac{5}{16}$ by 8 plate: $A_p = 2.50$ in.².

Properties of Trial Section

Steel section [from Eq. 2-1)]:

$$K_s = \frac{2.50}{2.50 + 44.16} = 0.0536$$

$$\bar{y}_s = \frac{1}{2}(35.84 + 0.31)0.0536 = 0.97 \text{ in.}$$

$$I_s = 0.97 \times 18.08 \times 44.16 + 9,012 = 9,786 \text{ in.}^4$$

$$y_{ts} = 17.92 + 0.97 = 18.89 \text{ in.}$$

$$y_{bs} = 17.92 - 0.97 + 0.31 = 17.26 \text{ in.}$$

$$S_{bs} = 570 \text{ in.}^3$$

Composite section [from Eq. (2-3)] with $k = 3$:

$$K_c = \frac{14.40}{14.40 + 46.66} = 0.2358$$

$$\bar{y}_c = (18.89 + 3)0.2358 = 5.16 \text{ in.}$$

$$I_c = 5.16 \times 21.89 \times 46.66 + 9,786 + \frac{14.40 \times 6^2}{12} = 15,100 \text{ in.}^4$$

$$y_{bc} = 17.26 + 5.16 = 22.42 \text{ in.}$$

$$S_{bc} = 674 \text{ in.}^3$$

Composite section with $k = 1$:

$$K_c = \frac{43.20}{43.20 + 46.66} = 0.481$$

$\bar{y}_c = (18.89 + 3)0.481 = 10.52$ in.

$I_c = 10.52 \times 21.89 \times 46.66 + 9{,}786 + \dfrac{14.40 \times 6^2}{12} = 20{,}570$ in.^{4}

$y_{bc} = 17.26 + 10.52 = 27.78$ in.

$S_{bc} = 741$ in.^{3}

$m = 43.20(18.89 - 10.52 + 3) = 491$ in.^{3}

Stresses

$$\text{DLs} = \frac{225 \times 12}{570} = 4.74 \text{ ksi}$$

$$\text{DLc} = \frac{70 \times 12}{674} = 1.25$$

$$\text{LL} = \frac{750 \times 12}{741} = 12.15$$

$$f_b = \overline{18.14 \text{ ksi}}$$

Cover plate is not needed at point 11.8:

$$f_b = \frac{170 \times 12}{502.9} + \frac{65 \times 12}{599} + \frac{690 \times 12}{662} = 17.87 \text{ ksi}$$

Shear Connector Spacing (using groups of four studs $\frac{3}{4}$ in. in diameter; see Example 4-1). From Eq. (3-3a), the useful capacity Q_{uc} of one stud is 10.2 kips and of one group

$$4Q_{uc} = 10.2 \times 4 = 40.8 \text{ kips}$$

Coefficients for computing the safety factor from Eq. (3-6) are:

	Point 3.5	Point 8	Point 13
C_{mc}	$^{78.4}\!/_{730} = 0.107$	$^{160}\!/_{650} = 0.246$	$^{70.4}\!/_{750} = 0.093$
C_{mi}	$^{270.4}\!/_{730} = 0.370$	$^{675.5}\!/_{650} = 1.038$	$^{225.4}\!/_{750} = 0.300$
C_s	$^{776.6}\!/_{592} = 1.311$	1.000	$^{741.4}\!/_{567} = 1.306$

At points 3.5, 8, and 13, respectively,

LLFS

$= 2.7(1 + 0.107 + 0.370 \times 1.311) - (0.107 + 0.370) = 3.82$

$= 2.7(1 + 0.246 + 1.038 \times 1.000) - (0.246 + 1.038) = 4.88$

$= 2.7(1 + 0.093 + 0.300 \times 1.306) - (0.093 + 0.300) = 3.62$

Use LLFS $= 3.62$ at all cross sections, and obtain the shear from Fig. 4-12.

Point 0 (composite—no cover plate):

$$V_{LL} + I = 51 \text{ kips}$$
$$V_{Dc} = \underline{\quad 5 \quad}$$
$$V_c = 56 \text{ kips}$$
$$C_v = \tfrac{5}{51} = 0.10$$
$$\text{FS} = \frac{3.62 + 0.10}{1 + 0.10} = 3.38$$

From Eq. (3-8), the pitch is

$$p = \frac{I_c}{mV_c} \frac{4Q_{uc}}{\text{FS}} = \frac{18,700}{457 \times 56} \times \frac{40.8}{3.38} = 8.82 \text{ in.}$$

Point 1 (composite—no cover plate):

$$V_{LL} + I = 41 \text{ kips}$$
$$V_{Dc} = \underline{\quad 4 \quad}$$
$$V_c = 45 \text{ kips}$$
$$C_v = \tfrac{4}{41} = 0.10$$
$$\text{FS} = \frac{3.62 + 0.10}{1 + 0.10} = 3.38$$
$$p = \tfrac{56}{45} \times 8.82 = 10.97 \text{ in.}$$

Point 2 (composite—cover plate):

$$V_{LL} + I = 32 \text{ kips}$$
$$V_{Dc} = \underline{\quad 2 \quad}$$
$$V_c = 34 \text{ kips}$$
$$C_v = \tfrac{2}{32} = 0.06$$
$$\text{FS} = \frac{3.62 + 0.06}{1 + 0.06} = 3.47$$
$$p = \frac{21,430}{504 \times 34} \times \frac{40.8}{3.47} = \frac{1,734}{34 \times 3.47} = 14.70 \text{ in.}$$

Point 3 (composite—cover plate):

$$V_{LL} + I = 25 \text{ kips}$$
$$V_{Dc} = \underline{\quad 0 \quad}$$
$$V_c = 25 \text{ kips}$$
$$C_v = 0$$
$$\text{FS} = 3.62$$
$$p = \frac{1,734}{25 \times 3.62} = 19.16 \text{ in.}$$

Point 4.5 (composite—cover plate):

$$V_{LL} + I = 27 \text{ kips}$$
$$V_{Dc} = \underline{3}$$
$$V_c = 30 \text{ kips}$$
$$C_v = \tfrac{3}{27} = 0.11$$
$$\text{FS} = \frac{3.62 + 0.11}{1 + 0.11} = 3.36$$
$$p = \frac{1,734}{30 \times 3.36} = 17.20 \text{ in.}$$

Point 5.5 (noncomposite—no cover plate):

$$V_{LL} + I = 34 \text{ kips}$$
$$V_{Dc} = \underline{5}$$
$$V_c = 39 \text{ kips}$$
$$C_v = \tfrac{5}{34} = 0.15$$
$$\text{FS} = \frac{3.62 + 0.15}{1 + 0.15} = 3.28$$
$$p = \frac{18,700}{457 \times 39} \times \frac{40.8}{3.28} = \frac{1,669}{39 \times 3.28} = 13.05 \text{ in.}$$

Point 10.5 (noncomposite—no cover plate):

$$V_{LL} + I = 37 \text{ kips}$$
$$V_{Dc} = \underline{4}$$
$$V_c = 41 \text{ kips}$$
$$C_v = \tfrac{4}{37} = 0.11$$
$$\text{FS} = \frac{3.62 + 0.11}{1 + 0.11} = 3.36$$
$$p = \frac{1,669}{41 \times 3.36} = 12.12 \text{ in.}$$

Point 11.5 (composite—no cover plate):

$$V_{LL} + I = 31 \text{ kips}$$
$$V_{Dc} = \underline{3}$$
$$V_c = 34 \text{ kips}$$
$$C_v = \tfrac{3}{31} = 0.10$$
$$\text{FS} = \frac{3.62 + 0.10}{1 + 0.10} = 3.38$$
$$p = \frac{18,700}{457 \times 34} \times \frac{40.8}{3.38} = 14.52 \text{ in.}$$

Point 12.5 (composite—cover plate):

$$V_{LL} + I = 25 \text{ kips}$$
$$V_{Dc} = \underline{\quad 1 \quad}$$
$$V_c = 26 \text{ kips}$$
$$C_v = \tfrac{1}{25} = 0.04$$
$$\text{FS} = \frac{3.62 + 0.04}{1 + 0.04} = 3.52$$
$$p = \frac{20{,}570}{491 \times 26} \times \frac{40.8}{3.52} = 18.67 \text{ in.}$$

Final Section

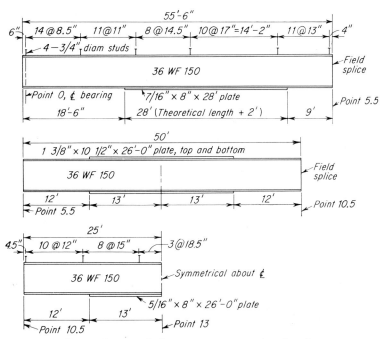

FIG. 4-15. Cover plates and shear-connector spacing for three-span continuous beam (Example 4-5).

Example 4-6. Four-span Continuous Bridge with Welded Plate Girders, No Shoring (girder $G2$, Fig. 4-16). The bridge in this example is made up of four continuous welded plate-girder spans and a concrete slab. Typical cross section of the bridge is shown in Fig. 4-16.

The web of the plate girders is of variable depth, as illustrated in Fig. 4-17.   The dimensions shown represent the first choice based on the dimensions of a similar structure.   The moment and shear curves are shown in Fig. 4-18; they were calculated from influence lines of a similar structure.   It is assumed for simplicity

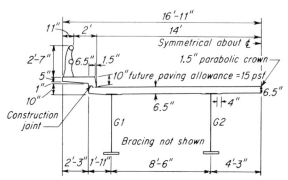

FIG. 4-16. Typical half section of bridge (Example 4-6).

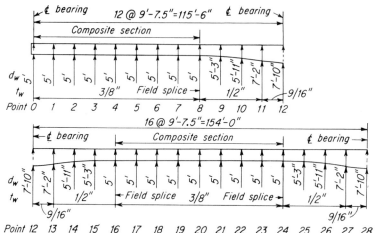

FIG. 4-17. Elevation of half of a four-span continuous beam, showing location of field splices and depth d_w and thickness t_w of web (Example 4-6).

that there is little difference in the relative elastic properties of the two structures.   Thus the need for calculation of a second set of moment curves is eliminated.

In selection of the points for reduction of the flange area in a welded girder, consideration should be given to the cost of making splices in relation to the cost of steel and to the plate lengths

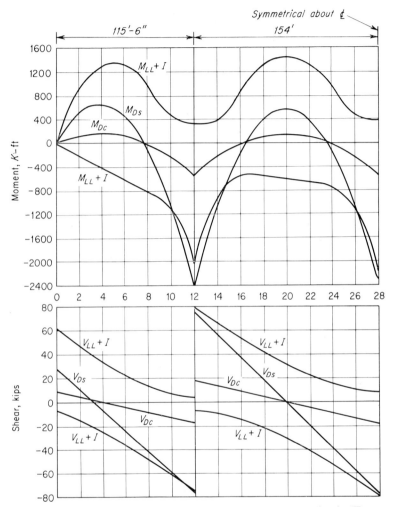

FIG. 4-18. Moment and shear curves for four-span continuous beam (Example 4-6).

available from the mills in the particular vicinity.   Calculations of the required flanges in the regions of negative moments are given for 9-ft 7.5-in. increments of length, to illustrate the possible flange reductions.   However, it is assumed in the final selection of the flange plates that the relative cost of splices is high.   Thus, the number of splices is kept to a minimum, in accordance with assumed available plate lengths—in this case, the first lengths given in Tables of Available Lengths in the "Steel Construction Manual" of the American Institute of Steel Construction.

Methods for calculating bearing stiffeners, intermediate stiffeners, weld sizes, bracing, erection stresses, and splice details are the same as for a noncomposite girder and are not given here.

Design Data

Spans: two 116 ft end spans and two 154 ft intermediate spans
Distances center to center bearings: 115 ft 6 in. end spans, 154 ft 0 in. intermediate spans
Live load = H20-S16-44
Live-load distributions = 8.50/5.5 = 1.545
Dead loads to girder $G2$:

Rail = 20 lb per ft $\times$ $\frac{3}{4}$	=	10.0 lb per ft
Sidewalk = 2.25 $\times$ 0.458		
@ 150 lb per ft^3 $\times$ $\frac{3}{4}$ =		77.3
Curb = 0.604 $\times$ 0.833 @ 150 lb		
per ft^3 $\times$ $\frac{3}{4}$ =		37.7
Future paving = 28 @ 15 lb		
per ft^2 $\times$ $\frac{1}{4}$ =		105.0
Dead load on composite section =		230 lb per ft
Deck slab = 8.50 $\times$ 0.542 @ 150 lb		
per ft^3 =		691.0
Slab coping, or haunch = 0.667 $\times$ 0.083		
@ 150 lb per ft^3 =		8.3
Bracing =		31.0
Dead load on steel beam alone less		
girder weight =		730.3 lb per ft
Estimated average girder weight =		270.0
Dead load on steel beam alone =		1,000 lb per ft

Positive-moment Sections—End Spans

Point 4—From Fig. 4-18:

Moments, kip-ft	Required section modulus, in.^{3}
M_{Ds} = 700	467
M_{Dc} = 180	120
$M_{LL} + I$ = 1,300	867

Assume $d_w = 60.00$ in., $t_w = 0.375$ in., $A_w = 22.50$ in.^{2}, $A_t/A_w = 0.3$, $A_b/A_w = 0.8$, $A_s = (1 + 0.3 + 0.8)22.50 = 47.2$ in.^{2}.

$$\frac{e_c}{d_w} = \frac{3.25}{60.0} = 0.054 \qquad\qquad \frac{S_{ts}}{(A_w + 2A_t)d_w} = 0.33 \text{ (Fig. 5-3)}$$

$$k_{Dc} = 3 \qquad\qquad\qquad\qquad\qquad k_{LL} = 1$$

$$A_c = \frac{bt}{kn} = \frac{6.50 \times 78}{3 \times 10} \qquad\qquad A_c = \frac{6.50 \times 78}{1 \times 10}$$

$$= 16.90 \text{ in.}^2 \qquad\qquad\qquad = 50.7 \text{ in.}^2$$

$$K_c = \frac{A_c}{A_c + A_s} = \frac{16.90}{16.90 + 47.2} \qquad K_c = \frac{50.7}{50.7 + 47.2}$$

$$= 0.263 \qquad\qquad\qquad\qquad = 0.518$$

From Fig. 5-10.

$$\frac{S_{bc}}{(A_w + 2A_b)d_w} = 0.396 \qquad \frac{S_{bc}}{(A_w + 2A_b)d_w} = 0.432$$

$$\frac{(A_w + 2A_t)d_w}{S_{tc}} = 1.25 \qquad \frac{(A_w + 2A_t)d_w}{S_{tc}} = 0.55$$

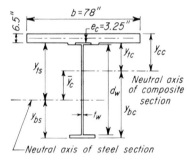

FIG. 4-19. Composite design section of $G2$ (Example 4-6).

First Trial Section [with Eq. (2-11), d_w assumed to be 60 in. and $A_w = 22.5$ in.^{2}]

Top flange:

$$A_{Ds} = \frac{467}{0.33 \times 60} = 23.51 \text{ in.}^2$$

$$A_{Dc} = \frac{120 \times 1.25}{60} = 2.50$$

$$A_{LL} = \frac{867 \times 0.55}{60} = 7.95$$

$$A_w + 2A_t = \overline{33.96 \text{ in.}^2}$$

$$A_w = -22.50$$

$$2A_t = \overline{11.46 \text{ in.}^2}$$

$$A_t = \frac{11.46}{2} = 5.73 \text{ in.}^2$$

$$\frac{A_t}{A_w} = \frac{5.73}{22.50} = 0.255$$

Bottom flange:

$$A_{Ds} = \frac{467}{0.33 \times 60} = 23.51 \text{ in.}^2$$

$$A_{Dc} = \frac{120}{0.396 \times 60} = 5.05$$

$$A_{LL} = \frac{867}{0.432 \times 60} = 33.45$$

$$A_w + 2A_b = \overline{\quad 62.01 \text{ in.}^2}$$

$$A_w = -22.50$$

$$2A_b = \overline{\quad 39.51 \text{ in.}^2}$$

$$A_b = \frac{39.51}{2} = 19.75 \text{ in.}^2$$

$$\frac{A_b}{A_w} = \frac{19.75}{22.50} = 0.878$$

The assumed values of A_t/A_w and A_b/A_w are close enough to the first trial values to make a second trial unnecessary.

At point 5 the total moment is the same as at point 4. However, the M_{Ds} at point 4 is greater than at point 5; therefore point 4 will require the greater section. A 12- by ½-in. top flange is selected to provide ample room for a group of four ¾-in.-diameter stud shear connectors:

Try a 12- by ½-in. top flange and 16- by 1¼-in. bottom flange: $A_t = 6$ in.², $A_b = 20$ in.², and $A_s = 48.5$ in.².

Properties of Trial Section

Steel section [Eq. (2-2)]:

$$\bar{y}_s = \frac{(60 + 1.25)20 - (60 + 0.50)6}{2 \times 48.5} = 8.89 \text{ in.}$$

$$I_s = \frac{1}{4}(61.25^2 \times 20 + 60.5^2 \times 6) + \frac{1}{12} \times 22.5 \times 60^2$$
$$- 48.5 \times 8.89^2 = 27{,}170 \text{ in.}^4$$

$$y_{ts} = 30 + 0.50 + 8.89 = 39.39 \text{ in.}$$

$$S_{ts} = 690 \text{ in.}^3$$

$$y_{bs} = 30 + 1.25 - 8.89 = 22.36 \text{ in.}$$

$$S_{bs} = 1{,}215 \text{ in.}^3$$

Composite section [Eq. (2-3)] with $k = 3$:

$$K_c = \frac{16.90}{16.90 + 48.5} = 0.2584$$

$\bar{y}_c = (39.39 + 3.25)0.2584 = 11.02$ in.

$I_c = 11.02 \times 42.6 \times 48.5 + 27,170 + \dfrac{16.90 \times 6.5^2}{12}$

$\quad = 50,010$ in.^{4}

$y_{tc} = 39.39 - 11.02 = 28.37$ in.

$S_{tc} = 1,763$ in.^{3}

$y_{bc} = 22.36 + 11.02 = 33.38$ in.

$S_{bc} = 1,498$ in.^{3}

$y_{cc} = 39.39 - 11.02 + 6.50 = 34.87$ in.

$S_{cc} = 1,434$ in.^{3}

Composite section with $k = 1$:

$$K_c = \frac{50.7}{50.7 + 48.5} = 0.511$$

$\bar{y}_c = 42.63 \times 0.511 = 21.79$ in.

$I_c = 21.79 \times 42.6 \times 48.50 + 27,170 + \dfrac{50.7 \times 6.5^2}{12}$

$\quad = 72,400$ in.^{4}

$y_{tc} = 39.39 - 21.79 = 17.60$ in.

$S_{tc} = 4,110$ in.^{3}

$y_{bc} = 22.36 + 21.79 = 44.15$ in.

$S_{bc} = 1,640$ in.^{3}

$y_{cc} = 39.39 - 21.79 + 6.5 = 24.10$ in.

$S_{cc} = 3,004$ in.^{3}

$m = 50.7(24.10 - 3.25) = 1,057$ in.^{3}

Stresses

	f_c, ksi	f_t, ksi	f_b, ksi
DLs	0	$\dfrac{700 \times 12}{690} = 12.18$	$\dfrac{8,400}{1,215} = 6.91$
DLc	$\dfrac{180 \times 12}{1,434 \times 30} = 0.05$	$\dfrac{2,160}{1,763} = 1.23$	$\dfrac{2,160}{1,498} = 1.44$
LL	$\dfrac{1,300 \times 12}{3,004 \times 10} = 0.52$	$\dfrac{15,600}{4,110} = 3.79$	$\dfrac{15,600}{1,640} = 9.51$
	$\overline{0.57}$	$\overline{17.20}$	$\overline{17.86}$

Point 2—From Fig. 4-18:

Moments, kip-ft	Required section modulus, in.³
$M_{Ds} = 530$	353
$M_{Dc} = 130$	87
$M_{LL} + I = 910$	607

Assume $A_t/A_w = (12 \times \frac{1}{2})/22.50 = 0.27$, $A_b/A_w = 0.60$.

$$A_s = (1 + 0.27 + 0.60)22.50 = 42.1 \text{ in.}^2$$

$\dfrac{e_c}{d_w} = 0.054$ $\qquad\qquad\qquad \dfrac{S_{ts}}{(A_w + 2A_t)d_w} = 0.315$ (Fig. 5-3)

$k_{Dc} = 3$ $\qquad\qquad\qquad\qquad\qquad\quad k_{LL} = 1$

$A_c = 16.90 \text{ in.}^2$ $\qquad\qquad\qquad\qquad A_c = 50.70 \text{ in.}^2$

$K_c = \dfrac{16.90}{16.90 + 42.1} = 0.2865$ $\qquad K_c = \dfrac{50.7}{50.7 + 42.1} = 0.546$

From Fig. 5-9:

$\dfrac{S_{bc}}{(A_w + 2A_b)d_w} = 0.379$ $\qquad \dfrac{S_{bc}}{(A_w + 2A_b)d_w} = 0.413$

$\dfrac{(A_w + 2A_t)d_w}{S_{tc}} = 1.34$ $\qquad \dfrac{(A_w + 2A_t)d_w}{S_{tc}} = 0.58$

First Trial Section [applying Eq. (2-11), with $d_w = 60$ in. and $A_w = 22.5$ in.²]

Top flange:

$$A_{Ds} = \frac{353}{0.315 \times 60} = 18.68 \text{ in.}^2$$

$$A_{Dc} = \frac{87 \times 1.34}{60} = 1.94$$

$$A_{LL} = \frac{607 \times 0.58}{60} = 5.87$$

$$A_w + 2A_t = \overline{26.49 \text{ in.}^2}$$
$$A_w = -22.50$$
$$2A_t = \overline{3.99 \text{ in.}^2}$$

$$A_t = \frac{3.99}{2} = 2.00 \text{ in.}^2$$

Bottom flange:

$$A_{Ds} = \frac{353}{0.315 \times 60} = 18.68 \text{ in.}^2$$

$$A_{Dc} = \frac{87}{0.379 \times 60} = 3.83$$

$$A_{LL} = \frac{607}{0.413 \times 60} = \quad 24.50$$
$$A_w + 2A_b = \quad \overline{47.01 \text{ in.}^2}$$
$$A_w = \quad -22.50$$
$$2A_b = \quad \overline{24.51 \text{ in.}^2}$$
$$A_b = \frac{24.51}{2} = 12.26 \text{ in.}^2$$

Try a 12- by ½-in. top flange and a 16- by ¾-in. bottom flange: $A_t = 6$ in.², $A_b = 12$ in.², and $A_s = 40.5$ in.².

Properties of Trial Sect on

Steel section [Eq. (2-2)]:

$$\bar{y}_s = \frac{(60 + 0.75)12 - (60 + 0.50)6}{2 \times 40.5} = 4.52 \text{ in.}$$
$$I_s = \frac{1}{4}(60.75^2 \times 12 + 60.50^2 \times 6) + \frac{1}{12} \times 22.5 \times 60^2$$
$$- 40.5 \times 4.52^2 = 22{,}480 \text{ in.}^4$$
$$y_{ts} = 30.00 + 0.50 + 4.52 = 35.02 \text{ in.}$$
$$y_{bs} = 30.00 + 0.75 - 4.52 = 26.23 \text{ in.}$$
$$S_{bs} = 857 \text{ in.}^3$$

Composite section [Eq. (2-3)] with $k = 3$:

$$K_c = \frac{16.90}{16.90 + 40.5} = 0.2944$$
$$\bar{y}_c = (35.02 + 3.25)0.2944 = 11.27 \text{ in.}$$
$$I_c = 11.27 \times 38.27 \times 40.5 + 22{,}480 + \frac{16.90 \times 6.50^2}{12}$$
$$= 40{,}010 \text{ in.}^4$$
$$y_{bc} = 26.23 + 11.27 = 37.50 \text{ in.}$$
$$S_{bc} = 1{,}067 \text{ in.}^3$$

Composite section with $k = 1$:

$$K_c = \frac{50.7}{50.7 + 40.5} = 0.556$$
$$\bar{y}_c = 38.27 \times 0.556 = 21.27 \text{ in.}$$
$$I_c = 21.27 \times 38.27 \times 40.5 + 22{,}480 + \frac{50.7 \times 6.50^2}{12}$$
$$= 55{,}630 \text{ in.}^4$$
$$y_{bc} = 26.23 + 21.27 = 47.50 \text{ in.}$$
$$S_{bc} = 1{,}171 \text{ in.}^3$$
$$m = 50.7(35.02 - 21.27 + 3.25) = 862 \text{ in.}^3$$

Stresses

$$DLs = \frac{530 \times 12}{857.0} = 7.42 \text{ ksi}$$

$$DLc = \frac{130 \times 12}{1,067} = 1.46$$

$$LL = \frac{910 \times 12}{1,171} = 9.33$$

$$f_b = \overline{18.21 \text{ ksi}}$$

Point 6—From Fig. 4-18:

Moments, kip-ft		Required section modulus, in.³
$M_{Ds} =$	490	327
$M_{Dc} =$	140	93
$M_{LL} + I =$	1,350	900

Use the same constants as for point 4 and substitute in Eq. (2-11):

Bottom flange:

$$A_{Ds} = \frac{327}{0.33 \times 60} = 16.47 \text{ in.}^2$$

$$A_{Dc} = \frac{93}{0.396 \times 60} = 3.91$$

$$A_{LL} = \frac{900}{0.432 \times 60} = 34.72$$

$$A_w + 2A_b = \overline{55.10 \text{ in.}^2}$$

$$A_w = -22.50$$

$$2A_b = \overline{32.60 \text{ in.}^2}$$

$$A_b = \frac{32.60}{2} = 16.30 \text{ in.}^2$$

Try a 16- by 1-in. bottom flange and 12- by ½-in. top flange. $A_t = 6$ in.², $A_b = 16$ in.², and $A_s = 44.5$ in.².

Properties of Trial Section:

Steel section [Eq. (2-2)]:

$$\bar{y}_s = \frac{(60 + 1)16 - (60 + 0.50)6}{2 \times 44.5} = 6.89 \text{ in.}$$

$I_s = \frac{1}{4}(61^2 \times 16 + 60.5^2 \times 6) + \frac{1}{12} \times 22.5 \times 60^2 - 44.5 \times 6.89^2$
$= 25,010 \text{ in.}^4$

$y_{ts} = 30 + 0.50 + 6.89 = 37.39 \text{ in.}$

$y_{bs} = 30 + 1 - 6.89 = 24.11 \text{ in.}$

$S_{bs} = 1,037 \text{ in.}^3$

Composite section [Eq. (2-3)] with $k = 3$:

$$K_c = \frac{16.90}{16.90 + 44.5} = 0.2752$$

$\bar{y}_c = (37.39 + 3.25)0.2752 = 11.18$ in.

$$I_c = 11.18 \times 40.64 \times 44.5 + 25,010 + \frac{16.90 \times 6.50^2}{12}$$

$$= 45,290 \text{ in.}^4$$

$y_{bc} = 24.11 + 11.18 = 35.29$ in.

$S_{bc} = 1,283$ in.^{3}

Composite section with $k = 1$:

$$K_c = \frac{50.7}{50.7 + 44.5} = 0.533$$

$\bar{y}_c = 40.64 \times 0.533 = 21.64$ in.

$$I_c = 21.64 \times 40.64 \times 44.5 + 25,010 + \frac{50.7 \times 6.50^2}{12}$$

$$= 64,320 \text{ in.}^4$$

$y_{bc} = 24.11 + 21.64 = 45.75$ in.

$S_{bc} = 1,406$ in.^{3}

$m = 50.7(37.39 - 21.64 + 3.25) = 963$ in.^{3}

Stresses

$$\text{DLs} = \frac{490 \times 12}{1,037} = 5.67 \text{ ksi}$$

$$\text{DLc} = \frac{140 \times 12}{1,283} = 1.31$$

$$\text{LL} = \frac{1,350 \times 12}{1,406} = 11.52$$

$$f_b = 18.50 \text{ ksi}$$

Point 8 (field splice)—From Fig. 4-18:

$M_{Ds} = -$	90 kip-ft	$-$ 90 kip-ft
$M_{Dc} =$	10	10
$+(M_{LL} + I) =$	1,010	
$-(M_{LL} + I) =$		-810
	930 kip-ft	-890 kip-ft

Because of the sign reversal at this point, 50 per cent of the minimum moment must be added to the maximum to obtain the design moment:

$$M = 930 + \frac{1}{2} \times 890 = 1,375 \text{ kip-ft}$$

The flange area for this noncomposite section, which is symmetrical, can be obtained from Eq. (2-13b):

$$A_t = A_b = \frac{1,375 \times 12}{18 \times 60} - \frac{60 \times \frac{3}{8}}{6} = 11.53 \text{ in.}^2$$

Try $15\frac{1}{2}$- by $\frac{3}{4}$-in. flanges, with $A_t = A_b = 11.62$ in.^{2}.

$$I_s = \frac{1}{12} \times 22.5 \times 60^2 + 2 \times 11.62(30 + 0.38)^2 = 28,200 \text{ in.}^4$$

$$S = \frac{28,200}{30.75} = 917 \text{ in.}^3$$

$$f_t = f_b = \frac{1,375 \times 12}{917} = 17.99 \text{ ksi}$$

Negative-moment Sections

Point 9: $d_w = 5$ ft 3 in. $= 63$ in., $t_w = \frac{1}{2}$ in., and $A_w = 31.5$ in.^{2}, from Fig. 4-18:

$$
\begin{aligned}
M_{Ds} &= -500 \text{ kip-ft} & &- & 500 \text{ kip-ft} \\
M_{Dc} &= - \ 90 & &- & 90 \\
+(M_{LL} + I) &= \ \ 670 & & & \\
-(M_{LL} + I) &= & &- & 910 \\
\hline
& \ \ + \ 80 \text{ kip-ft} & &-1,500 \text{ kip-ft} \\
M &= \frac{1}{2} \times 80 + 1,500 = 1,540 \text{ kip-ft}
\end{aligned}
$$

From Eq. (2-13b), we find the required flange areas to be

$$A_t = A_b = \frac{1,540 \times 12}{18 \times 63} - \frac{63 \times \frac{1}{2}}{6} = 11.05 \text{ in.}^2$$

Try 15- by $\frac{3}{4}$-in. flanges, with $A_t = A_b = 11.25$ in.^{2}.

$$I_s = \frac{1}{12} \times 31.5 \times 63^2 + 2 \times 11.25(31.5 + 0.38)^2 = 33,290 \text{ in.}^4$$

$$S = \frac{33,290}{32.25} = 1,032 \text{ in.}^3$$

$$f_t = f_b = \frac{1,540 \times 12}{1,032} = 17.91 \text{ ksi}$$

Point 10: $d_w = 5$ ft 11 in. $= 71$ in., $t_w = \frac{1}{2}$ in., and $A_w = 35.5$ in.^{2}. From Fig. 4-18:

$$
\begin{aligned}
M_{Ds} &= -1,040 \text{ kip-ft} \\
M_{Dc} &= - \ 200 \\
M_{LL} + I &= -1,070 \\
\hline
&-2,310 \text{ kip-ft}
\end{aligned}
$$

Applying Eq. (2-13b):

$$A_t = A_b = \frac{2{,}310 \times 12}{18 \times 71} - \frac{71 \times \frac{1}{2}}{6} = 15.77 \text{ in.}^2$$

Try 16- by 1-in. flanges, with $A_t = A_b = 16$ in.^{2}.

$$I_s = \frac{1}{12} \times 35.5 \times 71^2 + 2 \times 16(35.5 + 0.50)^2 = 56{,}380 \text{ in.}^4$$

$$S = \frac{56{,}380}{36.50} = 1{,}545 \text{ in.}^3$$

$$f_t = f_b = \frac{2{,}310 \times 12}{1{,}545} = 17.94 \text{ ksi}$$

Point 11: $d_w = 7$ ft 2 in. $= 86$ in., $t_w = \frac{1}{2}$ in., and $A_w = 43$ in.^{2}. From Fig. 4-18:

$$M_{Ds} = -1{,}680 \text{ kip-ft}$$
$$M_{Dc} = - \quad 350$$
$$\underline{M_{LL} + I = -1{,}340}$$
$$-3{,}370 \text{ kip-ft}$$

$$A_t = A_b = \frac{3{,}370 \times 12}{18 \times 86} - \frac{86 \times \frac{1}{2}}{6} = 18.95 \text{ in.}^2$$

Try 20- by $^{15}\!/_{16}$-in. flanges, with $A_t = A_b = 18.75$ in.^{2}.

$$I_s = \frac{1}{12} \times 43 \times 86^2 + 2 \times 18.75(45 + 0.47)^2 = 97{,}360 \text{ in.}^4$$

$$S = \frac{97{,}360}{43.94} = 2{,}216 \text{ in.}^3$$

$$f_t = f_b = \frac{3{,}370 \times 12}{2{,}216} = 18.25 \text{ ksi}$$

Point 12: $d_w = 7$ ft 10 in. $= 94$ in., $t_w = \frac{1}{2}$ in., and $A_w = 47$ in.^{2}. From Fig. 4-18:

$$M_{Ds} = -2{,}360 \text{ kip-ft}$$
$$M_{Dc} = - \quad 500$$
$$\underline{M_{LL} + I = -1{,}980}$$
$$-4{,}840 \text{ kip-ft}$$

$$A_t = A_b = \frac{4{,}840 \times 12}{18 \times 94} - \frac{94 \times \frac{9}{16}}{6} = 25.52 \text{ in.}^2$$

Try 20- by $1^5\!/_{16}$-in. flanges, with $A_t = A_b = 26.25$ in.^{2}.

$$I_s = \frac{1}{12} \times 47 \times 49^2 + 2 \times 26.25(47 + 0.66)^2 = 155{,}000 \text{ in.}^4$$

$$S = \frac{155{,}000}{48.31} = 3{,}210 \text{ in.}^3$$

$$f_t = f_b = \frac{4{,}840 \times 12}{3{,}210} = 18.07 \text{ ksi}$$

Point 13: $d_w = 7$ ft 2 in. $= 86$ in., $t_w = \frac{1}{2}$ in., and $A_w = 43$ in.^{2}.

$$M_{Ds} = -1{,}690 \text{ kip-ft}$$
$$M_{Dc} = - 350$$
$$\underline{M_{LL} + I = -1{,}360}$$
$$-3{,}400 \text{ kip-ft}$$

Try 20- by 1-in. flanges (see point 11):

$$I_s = 26{,}500 + 2 \times 20(43 + 0.50)^2 = 102{,}200 \text{ in.}^4$$
$$S = \frac{102{,}200}{44} = 2{,}323 \text{ in.}^3$$
$$f_t = f_b = \frac{3{,}400 \times 12}{2{,}323} = 17.56 \text{ ksi}$$

Point 14: $d_w = 5$ ft 11 in. $= 71$ in., $t_w = \frac{1}{2}$ in., and $A_w = 35.5$ in.^{2}.

$$M_{Ds} = -1{,}100 \text{ kip-ft}$$
$$M_{Dc} = - 210$$
$$\underline{M_{LL} + I = - 930}$$
$$-2{,}240 \text{ kip-ft}$$

Try 16- by $^{15}\!/_{16}$-in. flanges (see point 10):

$$I_s = 14{,}910 + 2 \times 15(35.5 + 0.47)^2 = 53{,}730 \text{ in.}^4$$
$$S = \frac{53{,}730}{36.44} = 1{,}474 \text{ in.}^3$$
$$f_t = f_b = \frac{2{,}240 \times 12}{1{,}474} = 18.24 \text{ ksi}$$

Point 15: $d_w = 5$ ft 3 in. $= 63$ in., $t_w = \frac{1}{2}$ in., and $A_w = 31.5$ in.^{2}.

$$M_{Ds} = -580 \text{ kip-ft} \qquad - 580 \text{ kip-ft}$$
$$M_{Dc} = - 90 \qquad\qquad - 90$$
$$+(M_{LL} + I) = 550$$
$$\underline{-(M_{LL} + I) = - 660}$$
$$-120 \text{ kip-ft} \qquad -1{,}330 \text{ kip-ft}$$
$$A_t = A_b = \frac{1{,}330 \times 12}{18 \times 63} - \frac{63 \times \frac{1}{2}}{6} = 8.82 \text{ in.}^2$$

Try 14- by $\frac{5}{8}$-in. flanges:

$$I_s = 10{,}420 + 2 \times 8.75(31.5 + 0.31)^2 = 28{,}130 \text{ in.}^4$$
$$S = \frac{28{,}130}{32.13} = 876 \text{ in.}^3$$
$$f_t = f_b = \frac{1{,}330 \times 12}{876} = 18.23 \text{ ksi}$$

Point 16 (field splice): $d_w = 60$ in., $t_w = \frac{3}{8}$ in., and $A_w = 22.5$ in.^{2}.

$$M_{Ds} = -140 \text{ kip-ft} \qquad -140 \text{ kip-ft}$$
$$M_{Dc} = 10 \qquad\qquad\quad 10$$
$$+(M_{LL} + I) = 920$$
$$-(M_{LL} + I) = \qquad\qquad\quad -530$$
$$\overline{790 \text{ kip-ft}} \qquad \overline{-660 \text{ kip-ft}}$$
$$M = 790 + \tfrac{1}{2} \times 660 = 1{,}120 \text{ kip-ft}$$
$$A_t = A_b = \frac{1{,}120 \times 12}{18 \times 60} - \frac{60 \times \frac{3}{8}}{6} = 8.69 \text{ in.}^2$$

Try 14- by $\frac{5}{8}$-in. flanges, with $A_t = A_b = 8.75$ in.^{2}.

$$I_s = \tfrac{1}{12} \times 22.5 \times 60^2 + 2 \times 8.75(30 + 0.31)^2 = 22{,}830 \text{ in.}^4$$
$$S = \frac{22{,}830}{30.63} = 745 \text{ in.}^3$$
$$f_t = f_b = \frac{1{,}120 \times 12}{745} = 18.03 \text{ ksi}$$

Positive-moment Sections—Interior Spans

Point 18 (composite): $d_w = 60$ in., $t_w = \frac{3}{8}$-in., and $A_w = 22.5$ in.^{2}.

$$M_{Ds} = 420 \text{ kip-ft}$$
$$M_{Dc} = 140$$
$$M_{LL} + I = 1{,}320$$

Try 16- by 1-in. bottom flange and 12- by $\frac{1}{2}$-in. top flange (see point 6).

$$\text{DLs} = \frac{420 \times 12}{1{,}037} = 4.86 \text{ ksi}$$
$$\text{DLc} = \frac{140 \times 12}{1{,}283} = 1.31$$
$$\text{LL} = \frac{1{,}320 \times 12}{1{,}406} = 11.27$$
$$f_b = \overline{17.44 \text{ ksi}}$$

Point 20: $d_w = 60$ in., $t_w = \frac{3}{8}$ in., and $A_w = 22.5$ in.^{2}.

$$M_{Ds} = 600 \text{ kip-ft}$$
$$M_{Dc} = 180$$
$$M_{LL} + I = 1{,}470$$

Try 16- by $1\frac{1}{4}$-in. bottom flange and 12- by 1-in. top flange (see point 4).

	f_t, ksi	f_b, ksi
DLs	$\dfrac{600 \times 12}{690} = 10.44$	$\dfrac{7,200}{1,215} = 5.93$
DLc	$\dfrac{180 \times 12}{1,763} = 1.23$	$\dfrac{2,160}{1,498} = 1.44$
LL	$\dfrac{1,470 \times 12}{4,110} = 4.29$	$\dfrac{17,640}{1,640} = 10.76$
	$\overline{15.96}$	$\overline{18.13}$

Point 22: $d_w = 60$ in., $t_w = \frac{3}{8}$ in., and $A_w = 22.5$ in.^{2}.

$$M_{Ds} = 420 \text{ kip-ft}$$
$$M_{Dc} = 140$$
$$M_{LL} + I = 1,340$$

Try 16- by 1-in. bottom flange and 12- by 1-in. top flange (see point 6).

$$\text{DLs} = \frac{420 \times 12}{1,037} = 4.86 \text{ ksi}$$
$$\text{DLc} = \frac{140 \times 12}{1,283} = 1.31$$
$$\text{LL} = \frac{1,340 \times 12}{1,406} = 11.44$$
$$f_b = \overline{17.61 \text{ ksi}}$$

Point 24 (field splice): $d_w = 60$ in., $t_w = \frac{3}{8}$ in., and $A_w = 22.5$ in.^{2}.

$$M_{Ds} = -140 \text{ kip-ft} \qquad -140 \text{ kip-ft}$$
$$M_{Dc} = 0 \qquad\qquad\quad 0$$
$$+(M_{LL} + I) = 960$$
$$-(M_{LL} + I) = \qquad\qquad\qquad -730$$
$$\overline{820 \text{ kip-ft}} \qquad \overline{-870 \text{ kip-ft}}$$

$M = 870 + \frac{1}{2} \times 820 = 1,280$ kip-ft

$A_t = A_b = \dfrac{1,280 \times 12}{18 \times 60} - \dfrac{60 \times \frac{3}{8}}{6} = 10.47$ in.^{2}

$I_s = \frac{1}{12} \times 22.5 \times 60^2 + 2 \times 10.31(30 + 0.34)^2 = 25,730$ in.^{4}

$S = \dfrac{25,730}{30.60} = 838$ in.^{3}

Try 15- by $^{11}/_{16}$-in. flanges, with $A_t = A_b = 10.31$ in.^{2}.

$$f_t = f_b = \frac{1,280 \times 12}{838} = 18.32 \text{ ksi}$$

Negative Moment Sections—Center Support

Point 25: $d_w = 5$ ft 3 in. $= 63$ in, $t_w = \frac{1}{2}$ in., and $A_w = 31.5$ in.^{2}.

$$
\begin{array}{rlr}
M_{Ds} = & -550 \text{ kip-ft} & - 550 \text{ kip-ft} \\
M_{Dc} = & -100 & - 100 \\
+(M_{LL} + I) = & 650 & \\
-(M_{LL} + I) = & & - 870 \\
\cline{3-3}
& & -1,520 \text{ kip-ft}
\end{array}
$$

Same as point 9: 15- by $^3/_4$-in. flanges.

Point 26: $d_w = 5$ ft 11 in. $= 71$ in., $t_w = \frac{1}{2}$ in., and $A_w = 35.5$ in.^{2}.

$$
\begin{array}{rl}
M_{Ds} = & -1,060 \text{ kip-ft} \\
M_{Dc} = & -220 \\
M_{LL} + I = & -1,110 \\
\cline{2-2}
& -2,390 \text{ kip-ft}
\end{array}
$$

$$A_t = A_b = \frac{2,390 \times 12}{18 \times 71} - \frac{71 \times \frac{1}{2}}{6} = 16.52 \text{ in.}^2$$

Try $16\frac{1}{2}$- by 1-in. flanges, with $A_t = A_b = 16.50$ in.^{2}.

$$I_s = \frac{1}{12} \times 35.5 \times 71^2 + 2 \times 16.50(35.5 + 0.5)^2 = 57,700 \text{ in.}^4$$

$$S = \frac{57,700}{36.5} = 1,580 \text{ in.}^3$$

$$f_t = f_b = \frac{2,390 \times 12}{1,580} = 18.15 \text{ ksi}$$

Point 27: $d_w = 7$ ft 2 in. $= 86$ in., $t_w = \frac{1}{2}$ in., and $A_w = 43$ in.^{2}.

$$
\begin{array}{rl}
M_{Ds} = & -1,650 \text{ kip-ft} \\
M_{Dc} = & -370 \\
M_{LL} + I = & -1,470 \\
\cline{2-2}
& -3,490 \text{ kip-ft}
\end{array}
$$

$$A_t = A_b = \frac{3,490 \times 12}{18 \times 86} - \frac{86 \times \frac{1}{2}}{6} = 19.88 \text{ in.}^2$$

Try 20- by 1-in. flanges.

$$I_s = \text{see point } 13 = 102,200 \text{ in.}^4$$
$$S = 2,323 \text{ in.}^3$$
$$f_t = f_b = \frac{3,490 \times 12}{2,323} = 18.03 \text{ ksi}$$

Point 28: $d_w = 7$ ft 10 in. $= 94$ in., $t_w = \frac{9}{16}$ in., and $A_w = 52.8$ in.^{2}.

$$M_{Ds} = -2,360 \text{ kip-ft}$$
$$M_{Dc} = - \quad 530$$
$$M_{LL} + I = \underline{-2,140}$$
$$-5,030 \text{ kip-ft}$$
$$A_t = A_b = \frac{5,030 \times 12}{18 \times 94} - \frac{94 \times \frac{9}{16}}{6} = 26.86 \text{ in.}^2$$

Try 20- by $1\frac{3}{8}$-in. flanges, with $A_t = A_b = 27.5$ in.^{2}.

$$I_s = \frac{1}{12} \times 52.8 \times 94^2 + 2 \times 27.5(47 + 0.69)^2 = 164,000 \text{ in.}^4$$
$$S = \frac{164,000}{48.38} = 3,390 \text{ in.}^3$$
$$f_t = f_b = \frac{5,030 \times 12}{3,390} = 17.81 \text{ ksi}$$

Shear Connectors. The first step is to find m and other properties for 16- by 1-in. flanges top and bottom at points 8, 16, and 24:

Steel section:

$$I_s = 6,750 + 2 \times 16(30 + 0.5)^2 = 36,520 \text{ in.}^4$$
$$y_{bs} = 30 + 1 = 31 \text{ in.}$$

Composite section with $k = 1$:

$$K_c = \frac{50.7}{50.7 + 54.5} = 0.482$$
$$\bar{y}_c = (31 + 3.25)0.482 = 16.51 \text{ in.}$$
$$I_c = 16.51 \times 34.25 \times 54.5 + 36,520 + \frac{50.7 \times 6.5^2}{12}$$
$$= 67,520 \text{ in.}^4$$
$$m = 50.7(31 - 16.51 + 3.25) = 899 \text{ in.}^3$$

Shear Connector Spacing (using groups of four studs $\frac{3}{4}$ in. in diameter; see Example 4-1)

$$4Q_{uc} = 10.2 \text{ kips} \times 4 = 40.8 \text{ kips}$$

	Point 4	Point 12	Point 20
C_{mc}	$\dfrac{180}{1,300} = 0.138$	$\dfrac{500}{1,980} = 0.253$	$\dfrac{180}{1,470} = 0.122$
C_{mi}	$\dfrac{700}{1,300} = 0.538$	$\dfrac{2,360}{1,980} = 1.192$	$\dfrac{600}{1,470} = 0.408$
C_s	$\dfrac{1,640}{1,215} = 1.350$	1.000	$\dfrac{1,640}{1,215} = 1.350$

From Eq. (3-7), the live-load safety factor at Points 4, 12, and 20, respectively, is

LLFS
$$= 2.7(1 + 0.138 + 0.538 \times 1.350) - (0.138 + 0.538) = 4.36$$
$$= 2.7(1 + 0.253 + 1.192 \times 1.000) - (0.253 + 1.192) = 5.16$$
$$= 2.7(1 + 0.122 + 0.408 \times 1.350) - (0.122 + 0.408) = 3.99$$

Use LLFS = 3.99 at all cross sections, and obtain shears from Fig. 4-18.

Point 0:
$$V_{LL} + I = 62 \text{ kips}$$
$$V_{Dc} = 9$$
$$V_c = \overline{71 \text{ kips}}$$
$$C_v = \tfrac{9}{62} = 0.15$$

Applying Eq. (3-6), we find the factor of safety to be

$$\text{FS} = \frac{3.99 + 0.15}{1 + 0.15} = 3.60$$

From Eq. (3-8), the pitch is

$$p = \frac{I_c}{mV_c}\frac{4Q_{uc}}{\text{FS}} = \frac{55,630}{862 \times 71} \times \frac{40.8}{3.60} = \frac{2,633}{71 \times 3.60} = 10.30 \text{ in.}$$

Point 1:
$$V_{LL} + I = 54 \text{ kips}$$
$$V_{Dc} = 7$$
$$V_c = \overline{61 \text{ kips}}$$
$$C_v = \tfrac{7}{54} = 0.13$$
$$\text{FS} = \frac{3.99 + 0.13}{1 + 0.13} = 3.65$$
$$p = \frac{2,633}{61 \times 3.65} = 11.83 \text{ in.}$$

Point 2:

$$V_{LL} + I = 46 \text{ kips}$$
$$V_{Dc} = 4$$
$$V_c = 50 \text{ kips}$$

$$C_v = \frac{4}{46} = 0.09$$
$$\text{FS} = \frac{3.99 + 0.09}{1 + 0.09} = 3.74$$
$$p = \frac{72,400}{1,057 \times 50} \times \frac{40.8}{3.74} = \frac{2,795}{50 \times 3.74} = 14.95 \text{ in.}$$

Point 3:

$$V_{LL} + I = 40 \text{ kips}$$
$$V_{Dc} = 2$$
$$V_c = 42 \text{ kips}$$

$$C_v = \frac{2}{40} = 0.05$$
$$\text{FS} = \frac{3.99 + 0.05}{1 + 0.05} = 3.85$$
$$p = \frac{2,795}{42 \times 3.85} = 17.29 \text{ in.}$$

Point 4:

$$V_{LL} + I = 33 \text{ kips}$$
$$V_{Dc} = 0$$
$$V_c = 33 \text{ kips}$$

$$C_v = \frac{0}{33} = 0$$
$$\text{FS} = \frac{3.99 + 0}{1 + 0} = 3.99$$
$$p = \frac{2,795}{33 \times 3.99} = 21.23 \text{ in.}$$

Point 5:

$$V_{LL} + I = 30 \text{ kips}$$
$$V_{Dc} = 2$$
$$V_c = 32 \text{ kips}$$

$$C_v = \frac{2}{30} = 0.07$$
$$\text{FS} = \frac{3.99 + 0.07}{1 + 0.07} = 3.79$$
$$p = \frac{2,795}{32 \times 3.79} = 23.05 \text{ in.}$$

Point 6:

$$V_{LL} + I = 36 \text{ kips}$$
$$V_{Dc} = 4$$
$$V_c = 40 \text{ kips}$$

$$C_v = \tfrac{4}{36} = 0.11$$

$$\text{FS} = \frac{3.99 + 0.11}{1 + 0.11} = 3.69$$

$$p = \frac{2{,}795}{40 \times 3.69} = 18.94 \text{ in.}$$

Point 7:

$$V_{LL} + I = 42 \text{ kips}$$
$$V_{Dc} = \underline{6}$$
$$V_c = \overline{48 \text{ kips}}$$

$$C_v = \tfrac{6}{42} = 0.14$$

$$\text{FS} = \frac{3.99 + 0.14}{1 + 0.14} = 3.62$$

$$p = \frac{64{,}320}{966 \times 48} \times \frac{40.8}{3.62} = 15.68 \text{ in.}$$

Point 8:

$$V_{LL} + I = 49 \text{ kips}$$
$$V_{Dc} = \underline{8}$$
$$V_c = \overline{57 \text{ kips}}$$

$$C_v = \tfrac{8}{49} = 0.16$$

$$\text{FS} = \frac{3.99 + 0.16}{1 + 0.16} = 3.58$$

$$p = \frac{67{,}520}{899 \times 57} \times \frac{40.8}{3.58} = 15.02 \text{ in.}$$

Points 16 and 24:

$$V_{LL} + I = 53 \text{ kips}$$
$$V_{Dc} = \underline{8}$$
$$V_c = \overline{61 \text{ kips}}$$

$$C_v = \tfrac{8}{53} = 0.15$$

$$\text{FS} = \frac{3.99 + 0.15}{1 + 0.15} = 3.60$$

$$p = \frac{67{,}520}{899 \times 61} \times \frac{40.8}{3.60} = 13.96 \text{ in.}$$

Points 17 and 23:

$$V_{LL} + I = 47 \text{ kips}$$
$$V_{Dc} = \underline{6}$$
$$V_c = \overline{53 \text{ kips}}$$

$$C_v = \tfrac{6}{47} = 0.13$$

$$\text{FS} = \frac{3.99 + 0.13}{1 + 0.13} = 3.65$$

$$p = \frac{64{,}320}{966 \times 53} \times \frac{40.8}{3.65} = 14.04 \text{ in.}$$

Points 18 and 22:

$$V_{LL} + I = 41 \text{ kips}$$
$$V_{Dc} = \underline{\quad 4 \quad}$$
$$V_c = \overline{45 \text{ kips}}$$

$$C_v = {}^4\!/_{41} = 0.10$$
$$\text{FS} = \frac{3.99 + 0.10}{1 + 0.10} = 3.72$$
$$p = \frac{72,400}{1,057 \times 45} \times \frac{40.8}{3.72} = 16.70 \text{ in.}$$

Points 19 and 21:

$$V_{LL} + I = 36 \text{ kips}$$
$$V_{Dc} = \underline{\quad 2 \quad}$$
$$V_c = \overline{38 \text{ kips}}$$

$$C_v = {}^2\!/_{36} = 0.06$$
$$\text{FS} = \frac{3.99 + 0.06}{1 + 0.06} = 3.82$$
$$p = \frac{2,795}{38 \times 3.82} = 19.25 \text{ in.}$$

Point 20:

$$V_{LL} + I = 31 \text{ kips}$$
$$V_{Dc} = \underline{\quad 0 \quad}$$
$$V_c = \overline{31 \text{ kips}}$$

$$C_v = {}^0\!/_{31} = 0$$
$$\text{FS} = \frac{3.99 + 0}{1 + 0} = 3.99$$
$$p = \frac{2,795}{31 \times 3.99} = 22.60 \text{ in.}$$

Final Sections

Figure 4-20 shows the connector spacing, flange-plate sizes, and web thicknesses to be used, based on the preceding calculations.

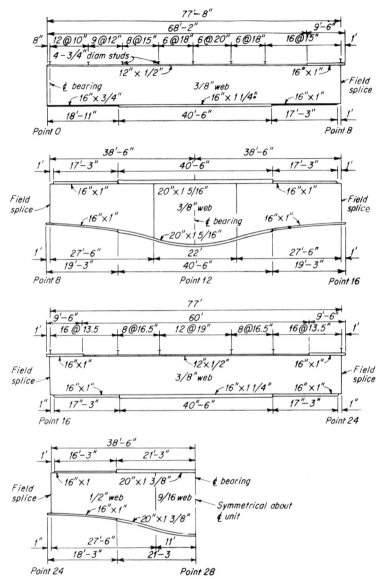

Fig. 4-20. Flange plates and shear-connector spacing for four-span continuous beam (Example 4-6).

CHAPTER 5

DESIGN AIDS

Concentrated in this chapter as a ready-reference section of design aids are all the curves and tabulated data used in the volume. The material thus grouped is just as easy for the first-time reader to refer to as it would be scattered throughout the text. And for the designer, not concerned with the elementary material in earlier chapters, the design aids may be more conveniently brought together in one chapter.

The following articles briefly explain the various tables and curves (except those which are obvious in meaning) and give pertinent text references.

5-1. Tables

The tables are self-explanatory for the most part. Table 5-1 gives moment of inertia I_c for a number of composite beams and I_B for the steel wide-flange beams incorporated in the composite members.

Table 5-2 contains a similar treatment of section modulus S_{bc} relative to the extreme fiber of the steel bottom flange in the composite section and S_s, the section modulus of the steel beam alone. (*Note:* $S_s = S_{bs} = S_{ts}$ for a symmetrical steel section such as a wide-flange beam.) A composite structure with wide-flange beams without cover plates can be designed from Table 5-2 by making use of the equation

$$S_{bc} = \frac{S_{bc}M_{Ds}}{S_{bs}f_b} + \frac{M_{Dc} + M_{LL}}{f_b}$$

from Art. 2-6. S_{bc}/S_{bs} may be approximated from Table 5-2. This design method is used in Example 2-1, Art. 2-11.

128

TABLE 5-1. MOMENT OF INERTIA
(Transformed to steel for $n = 10$, $b =$ effective slab width,
$t =$ slab thickness.)

Steel beam		Moment of inertia I_c of composite beams, in.[4]							
		$b = 5$ ft			$b = 6$ ft			$b = 7$ ft	
Shape	I_B, in.[4]	$t = 6$ in.	$t = 7$ in.	$t = 8$ in.	$t = 6$ in.	$t = 7$ in.	$t = 8$ in.	$t = 7$ in.	$t = 8$ in.
36 WF 300	20,290	32,062	34,056	36,085	33,648	35,820	38,017	37,386	39,715
36 WF 280	18,819	30,237	32,147	34,086	31,743	33,813	35,903	35,285	37,494
36 WF 260	17,234	28,265	30,083	31,926	29,682	31,646	33,624	33,019	35,104
36 WF 245	16,092	26,816	28,561	30,328	28,164	30,043	31,932	31,338	33,323
36 WF 230	14,988	25,403	27,076	28,766	26,683	28,477	30,279	29,696	31,583
36 WF 194	12,103	22,172	23,713	25,259	23,328	24,963	26,594	26,036	27,732
36 WF 182	11,282	21,028	22,496	23,967	22,116	23,668	25,215	24,670	26,274
36 WF 170	10,470	19,880	21,270	22,663	20,896	22,363	23,823	23,292	24,802
36 WF 160	9,739	18,845	20,172	21,500	19,805	21,198	22,586	22,066	23,498
36 WF 150	9,012	17,800	19,060	20,319	18,699	20,017	21,330	20,823	22,174
33 WF 220	12,312	21,334	22,806	24,298	22,425	24,001	25,591	25,038	26,703
33 WF 200	11,048	19,646	21,019	22,409	20,647	22,108	23,582	23,047	24,584
33 WF 141	7,442	15,002	16,099	17,200	15,754	16,899	18,047	17,572	18,753
33 WF 130	6,699	13,896	14,919	16,046	14,584	15,648	16,715	16,257	17,353
30 WF 124	5,347	11,376	12,255	13,145	11,939	12,855	13,781	13,355	14,309
30 WF 116	4,919	10,704	11,535	12,376	11,226	12,090	12,963	12,550	13,449
30 WF 108	4,461	9,983	10,763	11,553	10,463	11,271	12,090	11,692	12,533
27 WF 102	3,604	8,187	8,858	9,541	8,578	9,271	9,981	9,614	10,345
27 WF 94	3,267	7,612	8,234	8,871	7,964	8,608	9,269	8,916	9,597
24 WF 100	2,987	6,739	7,316	7,914	7,056	7,657	8,281	7,940	8,585
24 WF 94	2,683	6,379	6,936	7,512	6,681	7,260	7,861	7,527	8,148
24 WF 84	2,364	5,791	6,298	6,822	6,054	6,579	7,126	6,811	7,377
24 WF 76	2,096	5,292	5,757	6,239	5,524	6,005	6,508	6,210	6,730
21 WF 73	1,600	4,202	4,603	5,026	4,390	4,807	5,250	4,975	5,435
21 WF 68	1,478	3,955	4,334	4,733	4,127	4,521	4,939	4,675	5,111
21 WF 62	1,327	3,640	3,990	4,361	3,793	4,157	4,545	4,294	4,700
18 WF 60	984	2,834	3,137	3,464	2,957	3,274	3,619	3,389	3,751
18 WF 55	890	2,622	2,905	3,211	2,732	3,029	3,353	3,133	3,474
18 WF 50	801	2,412	2,674	2,959	2,510	2,786	3,088	2,879	3,199
16 WF 50	655	2,056	2,300	2,567	2,144	2,401	2,686	2,486	2,789
16 WF 45	583	1,876	2,100	2,349	1,953	2,190	2,456	2,268	2,551
16 WF 40	516	1,697	1,903	2,133	1,764	1,983	2,230	2,053	2,316
16 WF 36	446	1,532	1,723	1,937	1,592	1,795	2,027	1,859	2,107
14 WF 34	339	1,230	1,401	1,597	1,281	1,465	1,677	1,522	1,751
14 WF 30	290	1,096	1,253	1,435	1,141	1,311	1,510	1,363	1,579

TABLE 5-2. SECTION MODULUS FOR BOTTOM FLANGE OF I BEAM
(Modular ratio $n = 10$, b = effective slab width, t = slab thickness.)

Steel beam			Section modulus S_{bc} of composite beam, in.³							
			$b = 5$ ft			$b = 6$ ft			$b = 7$ ft	
Shape	S_s, in.³	S_s/A_B, in.	$t = 6$ in.	$t = 7$ in.	$t = 8$ in.	$t = 6$ in.	$t = 7$ in.	$t = 8$ in.	$t = 7$ in.	$t = 8$ in.
36 WF 300	1,105.1	12.5	1,306.0	1,340.3	1,375.2	1,325.8	1,361.5	1,397.7	1,379.0	1,416.9
36 WF 280	1,031.2	12.5	1,223.2	1,255.2	1,288.7	1,241.9	1,275.5	1,309.9	1,292.0	1,327.2
36 WF 260	951.1	12.4	1,136.1	1,166.9	1,198.4	1,153.1	1,185.2	1,217.4	1,200.3	1,233.5
36 WF 245	892.5	12.4	1,070.9	1,100.2	1,130.0	1,087.0	1,117.3	1,147.8	1,130.9	1,162.7
36 WF 230	835.5	12.3	1,007.7	1,035.4	1,063.8	1,022.7	1,051.2	1,080.6	1,064.4	1,094.0
36 WF 194	663.6	11.6	838.3	863.9	889.4	851.7	878.1	904.3	889.5	916.5
36 WF 182	621.2	11.6	788.5	812.7	836.8	801.0	825.8	850.7	836.3	861.7
36 WF 170	579.1	11.6	739.0	761.5	784.2	750.3	773.3	796.8	783.2	806.8
36 WF 160	541.0	11.5	695.4	716.8	738.6	706.1	728.2	750.4	737.0	759.5
36 WF 150	502.9	11.4	651.5	672.1	692.5	661.4	682.2	703.3	690.6	711.8
33 WF 220	740.6	11.4	902.5	929.2	956.6	916.1	943.8	971.9	955.6	984.3
33 WF 200	669.6	11.4	821.7	846.5	871.6	833.9	859.2	885.2	869.7	896.2
33 WF 141	446.8	10.8	581.9	600.9	620.3	590.5	609.9	629.7	617.2	637.4
33 WF 130	404.8	10.6	533.8	551.7	573.5	541.8	559.9	578.4	566.4	585.5
30 WF 124	354.6	9.7	472.8	489.6	507.1	479.7	497.1	515.0	503.0	521.3
30 WF 116	327.9	9.6	441.6	457.6	474.2	448.0	464.5	481.4	469.9	487.3
30 WF 108	299.2	9.4	408.8	423.9	439.4	414.7	430.2	446.1	435.3	451.6
27 WF 102	266.3	8.9	363.1	377.4	392.3	368.3	383.0	398.3	387.5	403.2
27 WF 94	242.8	8.8	334.4	347.7	361.6	339.0	352.8	367.1	356.8	371.7
24 WF 100	248.9	8.5	332.8	346.6	361.0	337.3	351.4	366.6	355.6	371.2
24 WF 94	220.9	8.0	308.0	321.4	335.5	312.5	326.3	341.0	330.3	345.6
24 WF 84	196.3	7.9	276.3	288.5	301.3	280.1	292.8	306.2	296.3	310.2
24 WF 76	175.4	7.8	249.9	261.2	273.2	253.3	265.0	277.5	268.3	281.3
21 WF 73	150.7	7.0	219.4	230.5	242.6	222.6	234.3	246.7	237.4	250.5
21 WF 68	139.9	7.0	205.1	215.7	227.1	208.1	219.1	231.1	222.0	234.6
21 WF 62	126.4	6.9	187.1	197.0	207.7	189.8	200.1	211.4	202.7	214.6
18 WF 60	107.8	6.1	164.2	174.2	185.0	166.8	177.2	188.8	179.9	192.3
18 WF 55	98.2	6.1	150.9	160.2	170.5	153.2	163.1	174.2	165.7	177.4
18 WF 50	89.0	6.1	137.7	146.5	156.1	139.8	149.1	159.6	151.5	162.7
16 WF 50	80.7	5.5	128.3	137.4	147.4	130.5	140.2	151.1	142.7	154.3
16 WF 45	72.4	5.5	116.2	124.6	134.2	118.1	127.3	137.5	129.6	140.6
16 WF 40	64.4	5.5	104.2	112.1	120.9	106.0	114.5	124.2	116.8	127.2
16 WF 36	56.3	5.3	93.6	101.0	109.5	95.3	103.4	112.6	105.6	115.6
14 WF 34	48.5	4.9	82.9	90.5	99.2	84.7	93.0	102.5	95.3	105.6
14 WF 30	41.8	4.7	73.5	80.6	88.7	75.2	82.9	92.0	85.2	95.2

TABLE 5-3. COEFFICIENT m/I_c FOR HORIZONTAL SHEAR
(Modular ratio $n = 10$, b = effective slab width, t = slab thickness.)

Steel beam	Coefficient $\frac{m}{I_c}$ of composite beam, 1/in.							
	$b = 5$ ft			$b = 6$ ft			$b = 7$ ft	
Shape	$t = 6$ in.	$t = 7$ in.	$t = 8$ in.	$t = 6$ in.	$t = 7$ in.	$t = 8$ in.	$t = 7$ in.	$t = 8$ in.
36 WF 300	0.0170	0.0183	0.0193	0.0184	0.0196	0.0205	0.0206	0.0215
36 WF 280	0.0176	0.0188	0.0198	0.0190	0.0201	0.0210	0.0211	0.0220
36 WF 260	0.0183	0.0195	0.0204	0.0196	0.0208	0.0216	0.0218	0.0226
36 WF 245	0.0188	0.0200	0.0209	0.0202	0.0213	0.0221	0.0222	0.0230
36 WF 230	0.0194	0.0205	0.0214	0.0207	0.0218	0.0226	0.0227	0.0234
36 WF 194	0.0212	0.0222	0.0230	0.0224	0.0233	0.0240	0.0242	0.0248
36 WF 182	0.0217	0.0227	0.0234	0.0229	0.0238	0.0244	0.0246	0.0251
36 WF 170	0.0222	0.0232	0.0238	0.0234	0.0242	0.0248	0.0250	0.0255
36 WF 160	0.0227	0.0237	0.0243	0.0239	0.0247	0.0252	0.0255	0.0259
36 WF 150	0.0233	0.0242	0.0248	0.0244	0.0252	0.0257	0.0260	0.0263
33 WF 220	0.0213	0.0225	0.0234	0.0227	0.0238	0.0246	0.0248	0.0255
33 WF 200	0.0222	0.0233	0.0242	0.0235	0.0246	0.0253	0.0255	0.0262
33 WF 141	0.0253	0.0261	0.0267	0.0264	0.0271	0.0276	0.0279	0.0283
33 WF 130	0.0261	0.0269	0.0273	0.0272	0.0279	0.0283	0.0286	0.0289
30 WF 124	0.0288	0.0296	0.0301	0.0299	0.0306	0.0309	0.0313	0.0315
30 WF 116	0.0295	0.0302	0.0306	0.0306	0.0311	0.0314	0.0318	0.0320
30 WF 108	0.0303	0.0309	0.0313	0.0313	0.0318	0.0320	0.0325	0.0325
27 WF 102	0.0331	0.0337	0.0340	0.0341	0.0346	0.0347	0.0352	0.0351
27 WF 94	0.0338	0.0343	0.0345	0.0348	0.0352	0.0352	0.0357	0.0356
24 WF 100	0.0361	0.0367	0.0369	0.0372	0.0376	0.0376	0.0383	0.0381
24 WF 94	0.0371	0.0376	0.0377	0.0382	0.0385	0.0384	0.0391	0.0388
24 WF 84	0.0381	0.0384	0.0383	0.0391	0.0392	0.0390	0.0397	0.0393
24 WF 76	0.0390	0.0392	0.0390	0.0399	0.0399	0.0395	0.0403	0.0398
21 WF 73	0.0436	0.0435	0.0432	0.0445	0.0442	0.0435	0.0447	0.0438
21 WF 68	0.0441	0.0440	0.0435	0.0450	0.0446	0.0438	0.0449	0.0439
21 WF 62	0.0449	0.0446	0.0439	0.0457	0.0451	0.0442	0.0453	0.0442
18 WF 60	0.0507	0.0501	0.0489	0.0514	0.0503	0.0490	0.0505	0.0489
18 WF 55	0.0514	0.0505	0.0492	0.0520	0.0508	0.0493	0.0509	0.0491
18 WF 50	0.0519	0.0509	0.0495	0.0525	0.0510	0.0494	0.0511	0.0492
16 WF 50	0.0566	0.0550	0.0531	0.0568	0.0552	0.0530	0.0551	0.0525
16 WF 45	0.0570	0.0554	0.0532	0.0573	0.0554	0.0528	0.0550	0.0522
16 WF 40	0.0575	0.0556	0.0532	0.0578	0.0554	0.0527	0.0550	0.0519
16 WF 36	0.0583	0.0561	0.0535	0.0583	0.0556	0.0526	0.0550	0.0517
14 WF 34	0.0635	0.0605	0.0571	0.0634	0.0599	0.0560	0.0591	0.0545
14 WF 30	0.0641	0.0607	0.0565	0.0636	0.0596	0.0553	0.0587	0.0541

Table 5-3 contains values of m/I_c for use in Eq. (3-1),

$$S = \frac{V_c m}{I_c}$$

where S is the horizontal shear in pounds per linear inch of steel flange at the junction of slab and beam and V_c is the vertical shear in pounds acting on the composite section.

Table 5-5 gives factors of safety (see Art. 3-5) for use in determining design loads of shear connectors in composite structures where no dead loads act on the composite section. Two sets of values are given—one set, under $A = 1.8$, is designed to assure composite action up to the yield point of a structural-grade steel beam proportioned for $f_s = 18,000$ psi; the other set, under $A = 2.7$, is designed to retain composite action for all levels of loading up to the ultimate capacity of a structural-grade steel beam proportioned for $f_s = 18,000$ psi.

5-2. Curves

The curves in the figures of this chapter are plots of equations that were developed in Chap. 2 for the design of composite structures.

The following references indicate explanatory text and illustrations of the use of the curves: Fig. 5-1, Arts. 2-11 and 2-12; Fig. 5-2, Art. 2-12; Fig. 5-3 to 5-15, Art. 2-13.

TABLE 5-4a. USEFUL CAPACITY Q_{uc} OF ONE STUD CONNECTOR
IN POUNDS
($h_s/d_s \geq 4.2$)

Stud diam, d_s, in.	Concrete strength, f'_c, psi			
	2,500	3,000	3,500	4,000
⅝	6,500	7,100	7,600	8,200
¾	9,300	10,200	11,000	11,700
⅞	12,600	13,800	15,000	16,000

TABLE 5-4*b*. DIMENSIONS OF CHANNEL SHEAR CONNECTORS

Channel type and size	Flange thickness, in.		Web thickness t, in.
	Max, h	Min	
American Standard:			
3-in.:			
4.1-lb	0.377	0.170	0.170
5.0-lb	0.377	0.170	0.258
6.0-lb	0.377	0.170	0.356
4-in.:			
5.4-lb	0.413	0.180	0.180
7.25-lb	0.413	0.180	0.320
5-in.:			
6.7-lb	0.450	0.190	0.190
9.0-lb	0.450	0.190	0.325
6-in.:			
8.2-lb	0.487	0.200	0.200
10.5-lb	0.487	0.200	0.314
13.0-lb	0.487	0.200	0.437
7-in.:			
9.8-lb	0.523	0.210	0.210
12.25-lb	0.523	0.210	0.314
14.75-lb	0.523	0.210	0.419
Car building:			
3-in.:			
7.1-lb	0.390	0.313	0.312
9.0-lb	0.390	0.313	0.500
4-in.:			
13.8-lb	0.531	0.469	0.500
Shipbuilding:			
6-in.:			
12.0-lb	0.413	0.337	0.313
15.1-lb	0.521	0.429	0.313
15.3-lb	0.440	0.330	0.340
16.3-lb	0.521	0.429	0.375
18.0-lb	0.530	0.420	0.375
7-in.:			
17.6-lb	0.521	0.429	0.375
19.1-lb	0.554	0.446	0.350
22.7-lb	0.554	0.446	0.500

TABLE 5-5. FACTORS OF SAFETY FOR $C_{mc} = C_v = 0$

C_{mi}	C_s										
	1.0	1.1	1.2	1.3	1.4	1.5	1.6	1.7	1.8	1.9	2.0
$A = 1.8$											
0	1.80	1.80	1.80	1.80	1.80	1.80	1.80	1.80	1.80	1.80	1.80
0.1	1.88	1.89	1.92	1.93	1.95	1.97	1.99	2.01	2.02	2.04	2.06
0.2	1.96	1.99	2.03	2.07	2.10	2.14	2.18	2.21	2.25	2.28	2.32
0.3	2.04	2.09	2.15	2.20	2.26	2.31	2.36	2.42	2.47	2.53	2.58
0.4	2.12	2.19	2.26	2.34	2.41	2.48	2.55	2.62	2.70	2.77	2.84
0.5	2.20	2.29	2.38	2.47	2.56	2.65	2.74	2.83	2.92	3.01	3.10
0.6	2.28	2.39	2.50	2.60	2.71	2.82	2.93	3.04	3.14	3.25	
0.7	2.36	2.49	2.61	2.74	2.86	2.99	3.12	3.24	3.37		
0.8	2.44	2.58	2.72	2.87	3.02	3.16	3.27	3.45			
0.9	2.52	2.68	2.84	3.01	3.17	3.33	3.49				
1.0	2.60	2.78	2.96	3.14	3.32	3.50					
$A = 2.7$											
0	2.70	2.70	2.70	2.70	2.70	2.70	2.70	2.70	2.70	2.70	2.70
0.1	2.87	2.90	2.92	2.95	2.98	3.01	3.03	3.06	3.09	3.11	3.14
0.2	3.04	3.09	3.15	3.20	3.26	3.31	3.36	3.42	3.47	3.53	3.58
0.3	3.21	3.29	3.37	3.45	3.53	3.62	3.70	3.78	3.86	3.94	4.02
0.4	3.38	3.49	3.60	3.70	3.81	3.92	4.03	4.14	4.24	4.35	4.46
0.5	3.55	3.69	3.82	3.96	4.09	4.23	4.36	4.50	4.63	4.77	4.90
0.6	3.72	3.88	4.04	4.21	4.37	4.53	4.69	4.85	5.02	5.18	
0.7	3.89	4.08	4.27	4.46	4.65	4.84	5.02	5.21	5.40		
0.8	4.06	4.28	4.49	4.71	4.92	5.14	5.36	5.57			
0.9	4.23	4.47	4.72	4.96	5.20	5.45	5.69				
1.0	4.40	4.67	4.94	5.21	5.48	5.75					

TABLE 5-6. NUMBER OF STUDS EQUIVALENT TO 1-IN. WIDTH OF CHANNEL

Stud diam d_s, in.	Size of channel							
	3 in. 4.1 lb	3 in. 6.0 lb	4 in. 5.4 lb	4 in. 7.25 lb	4 in. 13.8 lb	5 in. 6.7 lb	5 in. 9.0 lb	6 in. 8.2 lb
⅝	0.645	0.775	0.702	0.800	1.091	0.761	0.856	0.820
¾	0.448	0.538	0.488	0.556	0.757	0.528	0.594	0.569
⅞	0.329	0.395	0.358	0.408	0.556	0.388	0.437	0.418

TABLE 5-7. EQUIVALENT NUMBER OF STUDS FOR ONE PITCH OF SPIRAL
(f'_c = 3,000 psi.)

Stud diam d_s, in.	Diam of spiral bar		
	½ in.	⅝ in.	¾ in.
⅝	2.01	2.52	3.02
¾	1.40	1.75	2.10
⅞	1.03	1.28	1.54

TABLE 5-8. WEIGHTS OF STUD SHEAR CONNECTORS

Stud diam d_s, in.	Weight of shaft, lb per in.	Weight, lb, of 100 studs having in-place length of				
		3 in.	4 in.	5 in.	6 in.	7 in.
¾	0.125	49.0	61.5	74.0	86.5	99.0
⅞	0.170	64.0	81.0	98.0	115.0	132.0

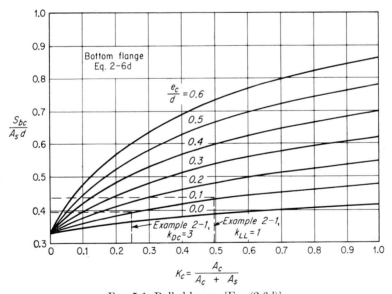

FIG. 5-1. Rolled beams [Eq. (2-6d)].

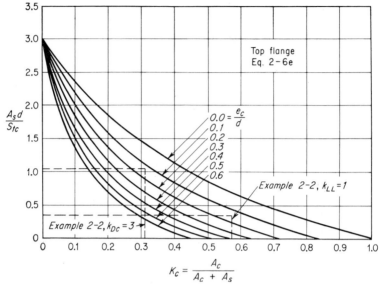

FIG. 5-2. Rolled beams [Eq. (2-6e)].

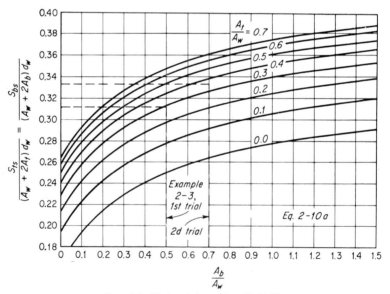

FIG. 5-3. Plate girders [Eq. (2-10a)].

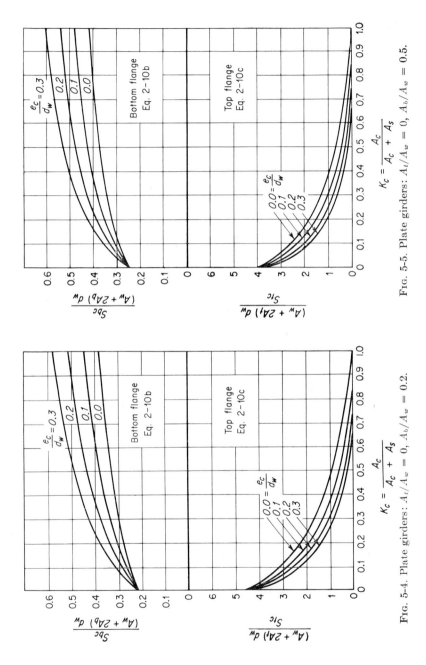

FIG. 5-4. Plate girders: $A_t/A_w = 0$, $A_b/A_w = 0.2$.

FIG. 5-5. Plate girders: $A_t/A_w = 0$, $A_b/A_w = 0.5$.

137

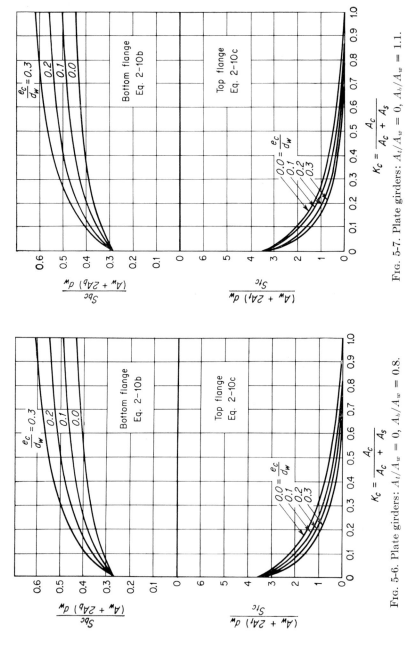

FIG. 5-7. Plate girders: $A_t/A_w = 0$, $A_b/A_w = 1.1$.

FIG. 5-6. Plate girders: $A_t/A_w = 0$, $A_b/A_w = 0.8$.

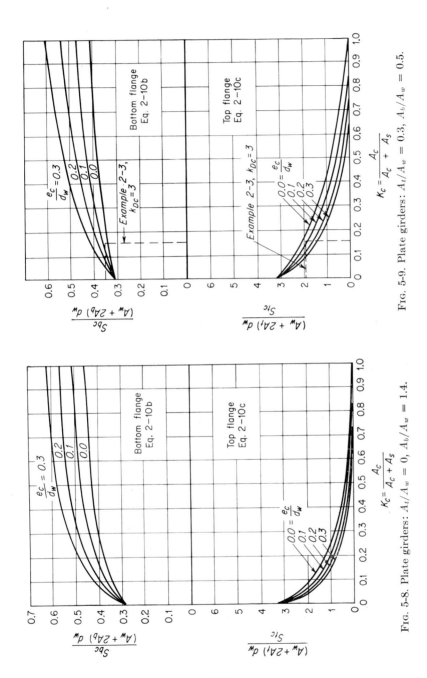

FIG. 5-9. Plate girders: $A_t/A_w = 0.3$, $A_b/A_w = 0.5$.

FIG. 5-8. Plate girders: $A_t/A_w = 0$, $A_b/A_w = 1.4$.

139

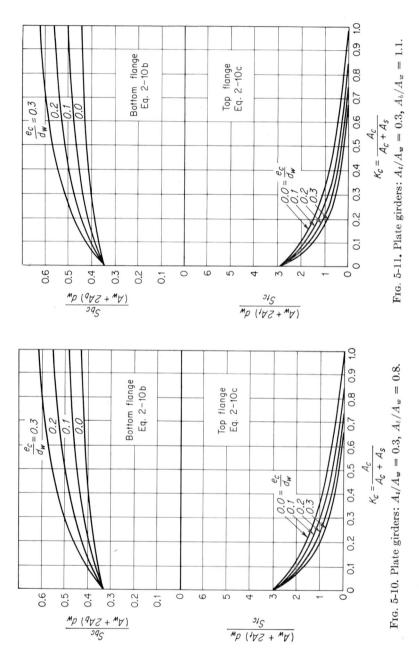

FIG. 5-11. Plate girders: $A_t/A_w = 0.3$, $A_b/A_w = 1.1$.

FIG. 5-10. Plate girders: $A_t/A_w = 0.3$, $A_t/A_w = 0.8$.

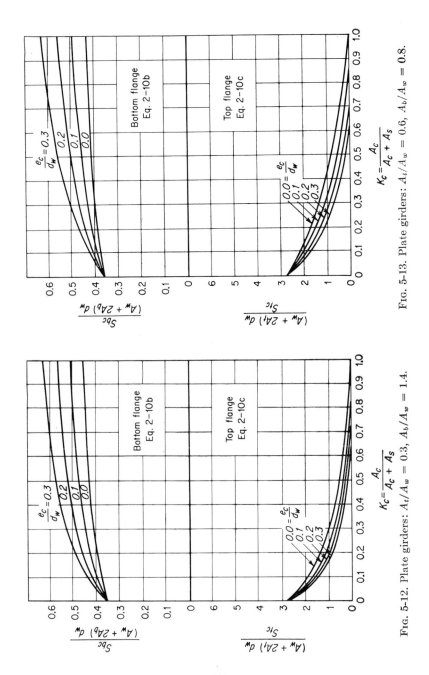

FIG. 5-12. Plate girders: $A_t/A_w = 0.3$, $A_b/A_w = 1.4$.

FIG. 5-13. Plate girders: $A_t/A_w = 0.6$, $A_b/A_w = 0.8$.

141

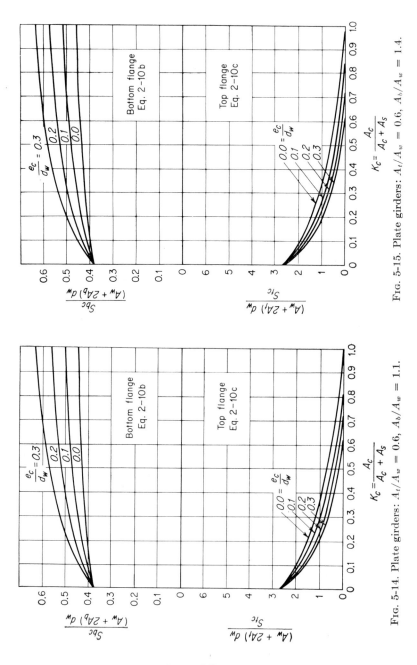

Fig. 5-15. Plate girders: $A_t/A_w = 0.6$, $A_b/A_w = 1.4$.

Fig. 5-14. Plate girders: $A_t/A_w = 0.6$, $A_b/A_w = 1.1$.

CHAPTER 6

LITERATURE

The design procedures in the preceding chapters are presented in a form aimed at ready use by the designer. For this reason, explanations of assumptions and derivations of equations are given only when not generally known or not easily found in existing literature. The reader who is interested in a more thorough study of the subject is referred to the references listed below.

The references are divided into three categories: research, design, and construction. The research papers include experimental reports, theoretical studies, and general discussions of research findings. The papers on design include presentations of design methods and general discussions of design assumptions. The references dealing with construction contain primarily descriptions of existing structures. Papers containing material fitting into two categories are listed twice. In each category, references are listed in chronological order.

Only American references are included, although a considerable wealth of information is available in foreign literature. A number of foreign references may be found in the selective bibliography in Ref. 14, Art. 6-1.

6-1. Research

1. Viest, I. M., R. S. Fountain, and C. P. Siess: Development of the New AASHO Specifications for Composite Steel and Concrete Bridges, *Highway Research Board Bull.* 174, 1957.
2. Hayes, J. M.: Vibration Study of Three-span Continuous I-beam Bridge, *Highway Research Board Bull.* 124, pp. 47–78, 1956.
3. Viest, I. M.: Investigation of Stud Shear Connectors for Composite Concrete and Steel T-beams, *Proc. Am. Concrete Inst.*, vol. 52, pp. 875–891, 1956.
4. Viest, I. M.: A Study of Shear Connectors for Composite I-beam

Bridges, *Proc. Southeast. Assoc. State Highway Officials*, pp. 96–114, 1955.

5. Viest, I. M.: Tests of Stud Shear Connectors, Parts I, II, III and IV, "Engineering Test Data," Nelson Stud Welding, Lorain, Ohio.

6. Viest, I. M.: Tests of Spiral Shear Connectors, "Engineering Test Data," Nelson Stud Welding, Lorain, Ohio.

7. Sinclair, G. M.: Fatigue Strength of ¾ Inch Welded Stud Shear Connectors, "Engineering Test Data," Nelson Stud Welding, Lorain, Ohio.

8. Viest, I. M., and C. P. Siess: Composite Construction for I-beam Bridges, *Proc. Highway Research Board*, vol. 32, pp. 161–179, 1953.

9. Siess, C. P., and I. M. Viest: Studies of Slab and Beam Highway Bridges: Part V—Tests of Continuous Right I-Beam Bridges, *Univ. Illinois Eng. Expt. Sta. Bull.* 405, 1953.

10. Fuller, A. H.: Effect of Trucks upon a Few Bridge Floors in Iowa in 1922 and 1948, *Highway Research Board Research Rept.* 14-B, pp. 1–9, 1952.

11. Foster, G. M.: Tests on Rolled Beam Bridge Using H20-S16 Loading, *Highway Research Board Research Rept.* 14-B, pp. 10–38, 1952.

12. Van Eenam, N.: Live-load Stress Measurements on Fort Loudon Bridge, *Highway Research Board Proc.*, pp. 36–57, 1952.

13. Lin, T. Y.: Load Distribution between Girders on San Leandro Creek Bridge, *Highway Research Board Research Rept.* 14-B, pp. 39–45, 1952.

14. Viest, I. M., C. P. Siess, J. H. Appleton, and N. M. Newmark: Studies of Slab and Beam Highway Bridges: Part IV—Full Scale Tests of Channel Shear Connectors and Composite T-beams, *Univ. Illinois Eng. Expt. Sta. Bull.* 405, 1953.

15. Siess, C. P., I. M. Viest, and N. M. Newmark: Studies of Slab and Beam Highway Bridges: Part III—Small Scale Tests of Shear Connectors and Composite T-beams, *Univ. Illinois Eng. Expt. Sta. Bull.* 396, 1952.

16. Fuller, A. H.: Skunk River Bridge Exhibits Composite Action after Twenty-eight Years of Service, *Civil Eng.*, vol. 21, no. 7, pp. 40–42, 1951.

17. Blumenschein, E. W.: Can Reliance Be Placed on Natural Bond between Concrete and Steel?, *Civil Eng.*, vol. 21, no. 7, pp. 42–43, 1951.

18. Newmark, N. M., C. P. Siess, and I. M. Viest: Tests and Analyses of Composite Beams with Incomplete Interaction, *Proc. Soc. Exptl. Stress Anal.*, vol. 9, no. 1, pp. 75–92, 1951.

19. Siess, C. P.: Composite Construction for I-beam Bridges, *Trans. Am. Soc. Civil Engrs.*, vol. 114, pp. 1023–1045, 1949.

20. Newmark, N. M., C. P. Siess, and W. M. Peckham: Studies of Slab

and Beam Highway Bridges: Part II—Tests of Simple-span Skew I-beam Bridges, *Univ. Illinois Eng. Expt. Sta. Bull.* 375, 1948.

21. Newmark, N. M., C. P. Siess, and R. R. Penman: Studies of Slab and Beam Highway Bridges: Part I—Tests of Simple-span Right I-beam Bridges, *Univ. Illinois Eng. Expt. Sta. Bull.* 363, 1946.

22. Hindman, W. S., and L. E. Vandergrift: Load Distribution over Continuous Deck Type Bridge Floor Systems, *Ohio State Univ. Eng. Expt. Sta. Bull.* 122, 1945.

23. Newmark, N. M., and C. P. Siess: Moments in I-Beam Bridges, *Univ. Illinois Eng. Expt. Sta. Bull.* 336, 1942.

24. Voellmy, A.: Strength of Alpha Composite Sections under Static and Dynamic Stresses, Porete Manufacturing Company, North Arlington, N.J.

25. Paxson, G. S.: Loading Tests on Steel Deck Plate Girder Bridge with Integral Concrete Floor, *Oregon Highway Dept. Tech. Bull.* 3, 1934.

26. Caughey, R. A.: Composite Beams of Concrete and Structural Steel, *Proc. 41st Annual Meeting, Iowa Engineering Society*, pp. 96–104, 1929.

6-2. Design

27. "Standard Specifications for Highway Bridges," 7th ed., div. I, sec. 9, The American Association of State Highway Officials, 1957, Washington, D.C.

28. Viest, I. M., R. S. Fountain, and C. P. Siess: Development of the New AASHO Specifications for Composite Steel and Concrete Bridges, *Highway Research Board Bull.* 174, 1957.

29. Fountain, R. S., and I. M. Viest: A Method for Selecting the Cross-section of a Composite Concrete and Steel T-beam, *Proc. Am. Soc. Civil Engrs.*, vol. 83, no. ST4, Paper 1313, 1957.

30. Subkowsky, H.: Choice of Composite Beams for Highway Bridges, *Proc. Am. Soc. Civil Engrs.*, vol. 83, no. ST1, paper 1151, 1957.

31. Villasor, Jr., A.: Computing the Properties of Composite Sections for Highway Bridges, *Civil Eng.*, vol. 26, no. 12, p. 67, 1956.

32. Fish, G. D.: Composite Construction Makes Sense, *Consulting Engineer*, May, 1956.

33. White, A.: Summary of Composite Bridge Beam Questionnaire Survey, *Proc. Am. Concrete Inst.*, vol. 52, pp. 1013–1014, 1956.

34. Viest, I. M.: Investigation of Stud Shear Connectors for Composite Concrete and Steel T-beams, *Proc. Am. Concrete Inst.*, vol. 52, pp. 875–891, 1956.

35. Viest, I. M.: A Study of Shear Connectors for Composite I-beam Bridges, *Proc. Southeast. Assoc. State Highway Officials*, pp. 96–114, 1955.

36. Sherman, J.: Continuous Composite Steel and Concrete Beams, *Trans. Am. Soc. Civil Engrs.*, vol. 119, pp. 810–828, 1954.
37. Viest, I. M., and C. P. Siess: Design of Channel Shear Connectors for Composite I-beam Bridges, *Public Roads*, vol. 28, no. 1, pp. 9–16, 1954.
38. Viest, I. M., and C. P. Siess: Composite Construction for I-beam Bridges, *Proc. Highway Research Board*, vol. 32, pp. 161–179, 1953.
39. "Alpha Composite Construction Engineering Handbook," 3d ed., Porete Manufacturing Company, North Arlington, N.J., 1953.
40. Newmark, N. M.: Design of I-beam Bridges, *Trans. Am. Soc. Civil Engrs.*, vol. 114, pp. 997–1022, 1949.
41. Siess, C. P.: Composite Construction for I-beam Bridges, *Trans. Am. Soc. Civil Engrs.*, vol. 114, pp. 1023–1045, 1949.
42. Newmark, N. M., and C. P. Siess: Design of Slab and Stringer Highway Bridges, *Public Roads*, vol. 23, no. 7, pp. 157–164, 1943.
43. Newmark, N. M., and C. P. Siess: Moments in I-beam Bridges, *Univ. Illinois Eng. Expt. Sta. Bull.* 336, 1942.

6-3. Construction

44. Scurr, K. R.: Welded-stud Shear Connectors for South Dakota Bridge, *Civil Eng.*, vol. 26, no. 6, pp. 38–40, 1956.
45. Fish, G. D.: Composite Construction Makes Sense, *Consulting Engineer*, May, 1956.
46. Page, Jr., P. P.: New Type of Shear Connector Cuts Costs of Composite Construction, *Eng. News-Record*, vol. 156, no. 19, pp. 46–48, 1956.
47. White, A.: Summary of Composite Bridge Beam Questionnaire Survey, *Proc. Am. Concrete Inst.*, vol. 52, pp. 1013–1014, 1956.
48. Continuous Girder Bridges Made Less Costly, *Eng. News-Record*, vol. 146, no. 22, pp. 36–37, 1951.
49. A Causeway Built to Withstand Hurricanes, *Eng. News-Record*, vol. 140, no. 16, pp. 568–571, 1948.
50. Cohen, A. B.: Repairs to Spruce Street Bridge, Scranton, Pennsylvania, *Proc. Am. Concrete Inst.*, vol. 43, pp. 241–248, 1947.
51. Wendell, E. W.: Welded Girder Bridge of Composite Design Carries Deck Area of Two Acres, *Eng. News-Record*, vol. 137, no. 26, pp. 856–858, 1946.
52. Willis, J. F.: Designs of Wilbur Cross Parkway Bridges, *Eng. News-Record*, vol. 136, no. 20, p. 792–797, 1946.
53. Enke, G. L.: Welding to Ensure Composite Beam Action, *Civil Eng.*, vol. 14, no. 1, pp. 9–12, 1944.

54. Willis, J. F.: Welded Plate Girder Bridge Separates Connecticut Highways, *Civil Eng.*, vol. 13, no. 9, pp. 407–408, 1943.
55. Cohen, A. B.: Major Bridge Replacement under Traffic, *Eng. News-Record*, vol. 128, no. 23, pp. 926–929, 1942.
56. Pavlo, E. L.: Strengthening Our Highway Bridges, *Eng. News-Record*, vol. 128, no. 9, pp. 339–342, 1942.
57. Bowden, E. W.: Roadways on Bridges, *Eng. News-Record*, vol. 120, no. 11, pp. 442–444, 1938.

APPENDIX 1

SUGGESTIONS FOR COMPOSITE DESIGN
FOR BUILDINGS

Composite design for buildings is usually based on the same principles as composite design for bridges. Thus, the methods presented in Chaps. 2 and 3 are applicable also to the design of buildings. However, differences in geometric layout, methods of construction, and loading conditions require certain modifications. These are discussed in the following articles.

No specifications are available for the composite design of buildings. It is general practice to use as guide the pertinent portions of specifications for steel buildings and concrete buildings. The 1952 "Specifications for the Design, Fabrication and Erection of Structural Steel for Buildings" of the American Institute of Steel Construction (AISC) and the 1956 "Building Code Requirements" of the American Concrete Institute (ACI) are followed in this book.

A-1. Methods of Construction

Temporary supports are used commonly in composite construction for buildings. However, usually the steel beams carry their own weight so that the structure is partially shored. Only the slab rests on temporary supports.

To make the construction fully shored, it would be necessary to induce with temporary supports an upward deflection of the steel beams prior to concreting the slab so as to eliminate the dead-load stresses caused by the beam weight. This is a delicate operation, which usually would have only negligible effect on the stress conditions and general design of the beams. *Use of full shoring is, therefore, not recommended for building construction.*

It is imperative to prevent movements of the temporary supports under the floor slab during construction until the concrete has reached 75 per cent of its 28-day design strength.

A-2. Design Assumptions

The width of the slab assumed effective as the flange of the composite T beam is usually taken as the smallest value given by the following conditions:

1. One-fourth the span of the beam.
2. The distance center to center of beams.
3. Sixteen times the least thickness of the slab. If the steel beam is fully encased, the effective width may be taken as sixteen times the least slab thickness plus the stem width.

The weight of the steel beam is carried by the steel beam alone. Therefore, an accurate design should be carried out as shown in part A of the design example in Art. A9. However, usually the weight of the steel beam is only a small fraction of the total design load, so it is sufficiently accurate to assume full shoring in the design computation. This approximation is illustrated in part B of the design example in Art. A9.

A-3. Loading Conditions

The live loads in building design are usually considered as uniformly distributed over the whole floor or roof area.

In some structures, such as warehouses and storage tanks, the live loads are kept on the structure for a long time. The computations of stresses due to live loads of long duration should account for creep; the modular ratio $n = E_s/E_c$ should be multiplied by a numerical factor $k = 3$.

For structures subjected to vibrations or impact, such as the effects of machinery or moving loads, the live loads should be increased to account for the dynamic effects.

A-4. Design of Beam Cross Section

In building construction, the use of rolled beams without cover plates is common, and the slab usually rests directly on the top flange of the steel beam ($e_c = t/2$). Thus, the cross section may be selected with the aid of Table 5-2 as explained in Art. 2-6.

For shored beams, $M_{Ds} = 0$. Thus, the required section modulus may be computed simply from

$$S_{bc} = \frac{M_{Dc} + M_{LL}}{f_b}$$

It should be noted, however, that this method neglects the effects of creep; so the actual required section modulus is a few per cent larger than indicated by this simple relationship.

In contrast to bridge design the slabs in building construction are occasionally very heavy compared with the steel beams. The following condition may exist (see also Art. 2-7):

$$\frac{d}{t} < \frac{1}{3}\frac{A_c}{A_s}$$

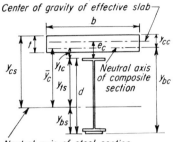

FIG. A-1. Composite beam with neutral axis in the slab.

If this is the case, computation of stresses should be based on the assumption that the concrete is cracked on the tension side of the neutral axis (Fig. A-1). The following formulas apply:

$$y_{cc} = \frac{knA_s}{b}\left[\left(1 + \frac{2y_{cs}}{knA_s/b}\right)^{\frac{1}{2}} - 1\right] \qquad (A\text{-}1a)$$

where A_s is the total area of the steel section.

$$A'_c = \frac{y_{cc}b}{kn} \qquad (A\text{-}1b)$$

$$\bar{y}_c = y_{cs} - y_{cc} \qquad (A\text{-}1c)$$

$$I_c = A'_c\frac{(y_{cc})^2}{3} + A_s(\bar{y}_c)^2 + I_s \qquad (A\text{-}1d)$$

$$y_{tc} = \bar{y}_c - y_{ts} \qquad (A\text{-}1e)$$

$$y_{bc} = \bar{y}_c + y_{bs} \qquad (A\text{-}1f)$$

$$m = A'_c(y_{tc} + e_c) \qquad (A\text{-}1g)$$

$$f_t = \frac{M_c y_{tc}}{I_c} = \frac{M_c}{S_{tc}} \qquad (A\text{-}1h)$$

$$f_b = \frac{M_c y_{bc}}{I_c} = \frac{M_c}{S_{bc}} \qquad (A\text{-}1i)$$

$$f_c = \frac{M_c y_{cc}}{knI_c}\frac{M_c}{knS_{cc}} \qquad (A\text{-}1j)$$

Equations A-1 are somewhat more tedious to use than Eqs. (2-3) based on uncracked section.   Fortunately, for most designs

$$\frac{d}{t} \geqq \frac{1}{3} \frac{A_c}{A_s}$$

in which case the simpler Eqs. (2-3) are applicable.

A-5. Continuity over Supports

When composite beams are connected to both sides of a girder and the slab is cast continuously over the girder, the slab will be forced to deform with the beams and cracking will result.   To prevent formation of wide cracks, negative reinforcement must be provided in the slab over the girder in the direction perpendicular to the girder.

In continuous design, the high moments and small section modulus over the supports may result in a rather inefficient design, even when the 20 per cent higher allowable steel stresses are used for the negative-moment section as permitted by the AISC specifications.   It is advisable, therefore, to increase the section modulus of the negative-moment section either by symmetrical cover plates or by a compression cover plate combined with increased reinforcement in the slab.

A-6. Deflections

In building design, the live loads are usually taken as uniformly distributed.   The live-load deflections may therefore be computed from Eqs. (2-14).

The live-load deflections should not exceed $\frac{1}{360}$ of the span if the beam supports a plastered ceiling.

It is suggested that the slenderness ratio of a composite beam be limited ordinarily to $\frac{1}{24}$ of the span and to $\frac{1}{20}$ of the span when vibrations or shock are present.   The slenderness ratios should be based on the over-all depth of the composite section.

A-7. Bond as Shear Connection

In buildings of light occupancy with no shock or vibrations and not subjected to overloading, failure of bond between the concrete slab and steel beam is unlikely to occur if the shearing stresses on the contact surfaces are low.   If, however, bond is destroyed at one location, progressive failure can be expected in time, and the result will be a complete or at least extensive spread of bond failure.

On the basis of available test information, it is recommended that the design bond stress be limited to 25 psi for unpainted hot-rolled steel surfaces. If bond exceeds this value at any location on the beam, the full horizontal shear *throughout* the beam should be assigned to mechanical shear connectors.

The bond may be computed from the horizontal shear as

$$u = \frac{S}{b'} \qquad (A\text{-}2a)$$

where

$S =$ the horizontal shear given by Eq. (3-1)
$b' =$ width of the top flange of the steel beam

Substituting from Eq. (3-1) gives the following expression for the bond stress:

$$u = \frac{V_c m}{b' I_c} \qquad (A\text{-}2b)$$

The statical moment m and the moment of inertia I_c should be computed with $k = 1$.

No reliance should be placed on bond if the contact surfaces of the steel are painted or the structure is subjected to shocks and vibrations or to large changes of temperature.

A-8. Mechanical Shear Connectors

Equation (3-6) for the factor of safety for mechanical shear connectors contains the numerical factor A which is inversely proportional to the allowable steel stress used in the design of the composite beam. If it is required to retain composite action up to first yielding of the steel beam, the allowable steel stress of $f_s = 20,000$ psi corresponds to $A = 1.65$. On the other hand, if it is required to retain composite action at all levels of loading, for $f_s = 20,000$ psi the value of $A = 2.4$ is necessary. The higher of the two factors is preferable, since it guarantees all advantages of composite action at the relatively low cost of a few additional shear connectors.

If the dead and live loads are distributed along the beam in the same manner (i.e., the shear diagram due to both types of load has the same shape), then the coefficients C_{mc} and C_v in Eq. (3-6) are equal. This is usually the case in building design.

Therefore Eq. (3-6) for the factor of safety reduces to

$$\text{FS} = \frac{A(1 + C_{mc} + C_s C_{mi}) - C_{mi}}{1 + C_{mc}} \qquad (A\text{-}3a)$$

It should be noted that Eq. (A-3a) gives a constant factor of safety at all points of the beam.

If full shoring is assumed in the design; i.e., $C_{mi} = 0$, Eq. (A-3a) reduces to a numerical constant

$$\text{FS} = A \qquad (A\text{-}3b)$$

Equation (A-3b) represents the minimum value of the factor of safety necessary for design of shear connectors. The maximum

TABLE A-1. FACTORS OF SAFETY FOR $C_{mc} = C_v = 0$ FOR BUILDING DESIGN

C_{mi}	C_s										
	1.0	1.1	1.2	1.3	1.4	1.5	1.6	1.7	1.8	1.9	2.0
$A = 1.65$											
0	1.65	1.65	1.65	1.65	1.65	1.65	1.65	1.65	1.65	1.65	1.65
0.1	1.72	1.73	1.75	1.76	1.78	1.80	1.82	1.83	1.85	1.86	1.88
0.2	1.78	1.82	1.85	1.88	1.91	1.94	1.98	2.01	2.04	2.08	2.11
0.3	1.84	1.89	1.94	1.99	2.04	2.09	2.14	2.19	2.24	2.29	2.34
0.4	1.91	1.98	2.04	2.11	2.17	2.24	2.31	2.38	2.44	2.50	2.57
0.5	1.98	2.06	2.14	2.22	2.30	2.39	2.47	2.56	2.64	2.72	2 80
0.6	2.04	2.14	2.24	2.34	2.44	2.54	2.64	2.74	2.84	2.93	
0.7	2.10	2.22	2.34	2.45	2.56	2.68	2.80	2.92	3.03		
0.8	2.17	2.30	2.44	2.57	2.70	2.83	2.96	3.10			
0.9	2.24	2.38	2.53	2.68	2.83	2.98	3.13				
1.0	2.30	2.47	2.63	2.80	2.96	3.13					
$A = 2.4$											
0	2.40	2.40	2.40	2.40	2.40	2.40	2.40	2.40	2.40	2.40	2.40
0.1	2.54	2.56	2.59	2.61	2.64	2.66	2.68	2.71	2.74	2.76	2.78
0.2	2.68	2.73	2.78	2.82	2.88	2.92	2.97	3.02	3.06	3.12	3.16
0.3	2.82	2.89	2.96	3.04	3.11	3.18	3.26	3.32	3.40	3.47	3.54
0.4	2.96	3.06	3.15	3.25	3.34	3.44	3.54	3.63	3.73	3.82	3.92
0.5	3.10	3.22	3.34	3.46	3.58	3.70	3.82	3.94	4.06	4.18	4.30
0.6	3.24	3.39	3.53	3.67	3.82	3.96	4.11	4.25	4.40	4.54	
0.7	3.38	3.55	3.72	3.89	4.05	4.22	4.39	4.56	4.73		
0.8	3.52	3.72	3.91	4.10	4.29	4.49	4.68	4.87			
0.9	3.66	3.88	4.10	4.31	4.53	4.74	4.96				
1.0	3.80	4.04	4.28	4.52	4.76	5.00					

value of the factor of safety may be obtained from Eq. (3-6) by assuming $C_{mc} = C_v = 0$ (special case of no temporary supports and no superimposed dead loads). Some numerical values of the maximum factor of safety are listed in Table A-1. On the basis of this table, an upper limit of FS = 3.5 appears reasonable for building design. Accordingly, *the range of factors of safety 2.4 to 3.5 is recommended for the design of shear connectors for buildings.*

It has been pointed out that in building construction the slab forms are usually shored; i.e., they are supported from the floor below. The slab represents the major portion of the total dead load, so that the parameter C_{mi} in Eq. (A-3a) is usually a very small quantity. Therefore, the factor of safety for the design of shear connectors for buildings is rarely much in excess of 2.4.

A-9. Examples of Composite Design for Buildings

Design of composite beams and shear connectors for buildings is illustrated by the following example of a typical warehouse corner bay, 30 by 30 ft between centers of columns. In building construction, the steel beams usually support their own weight, but the slab is shored so that the weight of the slab is carried by the composite section. Computations based on this partly shored construction are presented in part A of the example. Part B contains a redesign of one beam on the assumption of full shoring.

All beams are designed for simple supports. It is assumed that the average long-time live load is equal to 50 per cent of the total live load; therefore, $k = 3$ is used for one-half of the live load and $k = 1$ is used for the remaining half.

The design, where applicable, is made in accordance with the 1952 "Specifications for the Design, Fabrication and Erection of Structural Steel for Buildings" of the AISC and the 1956 "Building Code Requirements" of the ACI. A 3,000-psi concrete and structural-grade steel are used, with allowable stresses of 1,350 and 20,000 psi, respectively. The modular ratio is taken as $n = 10$.

The example illustrates selection of the steel cross section, computation of stresses, and design of shear connectors for all stringers and beams in the bay. The main carrying beams, $G1$ and $G2$, are designed as composite; however, it should be pointed out that if the stringers $S2$ are subjected to excessive deflections, cracks are likely to occur over beams $G1$ and $G2$. It is therefore suggested that a minimum of 1.0 per cent of reinforcement be placed in the top of the slab over those members and extended a minimum distance equal to the effective flange width.

A. Design for Partly Shored Construction

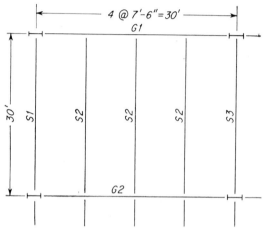

FIG. A-2. Framing plan of a corner bay of a building.

Design Data

Live load = 300 lb per ft²
Floor slab thickness = 4 in.

S2 and **S3**—Assume stringer weight = 70 lb per ft:

$$\text{DLs} = \qquad 70 \text{ lb per ft}$$
$$\text{DLc} = \quad 375$$
$$\text{LL } (k = 3) = {}^{300}\!\!/_{\!2} \times 7.5 = 1{,}125$$
$$\overline{\text{DLc} + \text{LL } (k = 3)} = 1{,}500 \text{ lb per ft}$$
$$\text{LL } (k = 1) = {}^{300}\!\!/_{\!2} \times 7.5 = 1{,}125 \text{ lb per ft}$$

Effective slab width = 16 × 4 = 64 in.

Selection of Trial Section

$$M_{Ds} = 0.070 \times 30^2 \times \tfrac{1}{8} = 7.9 \text{ kip-ft}$$
$$S_{Ds} = 7.9 \times {}^{12}\!\!/_{\!20} = 4.7 \text{ in.}^3$$
$$M_{Dc} + M_{LL} \ (k = 3) = 1{,}500 \times 30^2 \times \tfrac{1}{8} = 168.8 \text{ kip-ft}$$
$$S_{LL} \ (k = 3) = 168.8 \times {}^{12}\!\!/_{\!20} = 101.3 \text{ in.}^3$$
$$M_{LL} \ (k = 1) = 1{,}125 \times 30^2 \times \tfrac{1}{8} = 126.7 \text{ kip-ft}$$
$$S_{LL} \ (k = 1) = 126.7 \times {}^{12}\!\!/_{\!20} = 75.9 \text{ in.}^3$$

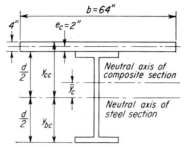

FIG. A-3. Design section for stringers $S2$ and $S3$ without shoring.

Assume 21 WF 62 with $A_s = 18.23$ in.^{2}, $d = 20.99$ in.,

$$I_s = 1326.8 \text{ in.}^4, \text{ and } S_s = 126.4 \text{ in.}^3$$

$$\frac{e_c}{d} = \frac{2.00}{20.99} = 0.0952 \qquad \frac{S_s}{A_s} = \frac{126.4}{18.23} = 6.94$$

$k = 3$:

$$A_c = \frac{64 \times 4}{3 \times 10} = 8.53$$

$$K_c = \frac{8.53}{8.53 + 18.23} = 0.319$$

$k = 1$:

$$A_c = \frac{64 \times 4}{1 \times 10} = 25.60$$

$$K_c = \frac{25.60}{25.60 + 18.23} = 0.584$$

From Fig. 5-1 for $k = 3$ and 1, respectively:

$$\frac{S_{bc}}{A_s d} = 0.403 \qquad \frac{S_{bc}}{A_s d} = 0.440$$

Bottom flange:

$$A_{Ds} = \frac{4.71}{6.94} \qquad\qquad = \quad 0.68 \text{ in.}^2$$

$$A_{Dc} + A_{LL} \ (k = 3) = \frac{101.3}{0.403 \times 20.99} = 11.98$$

$$A_{LL} \ (k = 1) = \frac{75.9}{0.440 \times 20.99} = \quad 8.21$$

$$\overline{20.87 \text{ in.}^2}$$

Try 21 WF 73 with $A_s = 21.46$ in.^{2}, $d = 21.24$ in.,

$$I_s = 1600.3 \text{ in.}^4, \ S_s = 150.7 \text{ in.}^3$$

Properties of Trial Section

Composite section with $k = 3$:

$$K_c = \frac{8.53}{8.53 + 21.46} = 0.284$$

$\bar{y}_c = (10.73 + 2.00)0.284 = 3.62 \text{ in.}$

$I_c = 3.62 \times 12.73 \times 21.46 + 1,600.3 + \dfrac{8.53 \times 4^2}{12} = 2,602 \text{ in.}^4$

$y_{bc} = 10.73 + 3.62 = 14.35 \text{ in.}$

$S_{bc} = 181.2 \text{ in.}^3$

Composite section with $k = 1$:

$$K_c = \frac{25.6}{25.6 + 21.46} = 0.543$$

$\bar{y}_c = 12.73 \times 0.543 = 6.92 \text{ in.}$

$I_c = 6.92 \times 12.73 \times 21.46 + 1600.3 + \dfrac{25.6 \times 4^2}{12} = 3,525 \text{ in.}^4$

$y_{bc} = 10.73 + 6.92 = 17.65 \text{ in.}$

$S_{bc} = 199.6 \text{ in.}^3$

$m = 25.6(10.73 - 6.92 + 2.00) = 148.5 \text{ in.}^3$

Stresses

$$\text{DLs} = \frac{7.87 \times 12}{150.7} = 0.63 \text{ ksi}$$

$$\text{DLc} + \text{LL} \ (k = 3) = \frac{168.8 \times 12}{181.2} = 11.17$$

$$\text{LL} \ (k = 1) = \frac{126.7 \times 12}{199.6} = 7.62$$

$$\overline{19.42 \text{ ksi}}$$

Maximum Bond Stress.   Maximum bond stress occurs at the support where shear V_c is the largest:

$$V_c = \frac{1}{2}(375 + 2 \times 1,125)30 = 39,400 \text{ lb}$$

$$u = \frac{V_c m}{b I_c} = \frac{39,400 \times 148.5}{8.30 \times 3525} = 200 \text{ psi}$$

Since the allowable bond stress of 25 psi is exceeded, the full horizontal shear must be transferred by mechanical shear connectors.

Shear Connector Spacing. Two ¾-in.-diameter studs per group ($h/d < 4.0$):

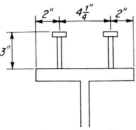

FIG. A-4. Stud location on $S2$ and $S3$.

$$Q_{uc} = 80 \times 3 \times \tfrac{3}{4} \sqrt{3,000} = 9,750 \text{ lb}$$
$$2Q_{uc} = 19.5 \text{ kips}$$
$$\text{FS} = \frac{2.4(1 + C_{mc} + C_{mi}C_s) - C_{mi}}{1 + C_{mc}}$$
$$C_{mc} = \frac{M_{Dc}}{M_{LL}} = \frac{42.1}{253.4} = 0.166$$
$$C_{mi} = \frac{M_{Ds}}{M_{LL}} = \frac{7.87}{253.4} = 0.031$$
$$C_s = \frac{S_{bc}}{S_{bs}} = \frac{199.6}{126.4} = 1.578$$
$$\text{FS} = \frac{2.4(1 + 0.166 + 0.031 \times 1.578) - 0.031}{1 + 0.166} = 2.47$$
$$p = \frac{I_c}{mV_c} \times \frac{2Q_{uc}}{\text{FS}} = \frac{3,525}{148.5} \times \frac{19.5}{2.47} \times \frac{1}{V_c} = \frac{187.3}{V_c}$$

At the center line of bearing:

$$V_{LL} = 2.25 \times 30 \times \tfrac{1}{2} = 33.8 \text{ kips}$$
$$V_{Dc} = 0.375 \times 30 \times \tfrac{1}{2} = 5.6$$
$$\overline{\phantom{V_{Dc} = 0.375 \times 30 \times}\; V_c = 39.4 \text{ kips}}$$
$$p = \frac{187.3}{39.4} = 4.76 \text{ in.}$$

At 5 ft from the center line of bearing:

$$V_{LL} = 2.25 \times 20 \times \tfrac{1}{2} = 22.5 \text{ kips}$$
$$V_{Dc} = 0.375 \times 20 \times \tfrac{1}{2} = 3.8$$
$$\overline{\phantom{V_{Dc} = 0.375 \times 20 \times}\; V_c = 26.3 \text{ kips}}$$
$$p = \frac{187.3}{26.3} = 7.14 \text{ in.}$$

At 10 ft from the center line of bearing:

$$V_{LL} = 2.25 \times 10 \times \tfrac{1}{2} = 11.25 \text{ kips}$$
$$V_{Dc} = 0.375 \times 10 \times \tfrac{1}{2} = \underline{1.88}$$
$$V_c = \overline{13.13 \text{ kips}}$$

$$p = \frac{187.3}{13.13} = 14.28 \text{ in.}$$

Final Section

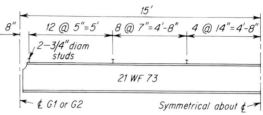

Fig. A-5. Stud spacing on *S2* and *S3*.

S1—Assume stringer weight = 60 lb per ft.

Design Data

$$\text{DLs} = 60 \text{ lb per ft}$$

$$\text{DLc} = 50(3.75 + 0.58) = 217$$
$$\text{LL } (k = 3) = {}^{300}\!\!/_{2}(3.75 + 0.58) = \underline{650}$$
$$\text{DLc} + \text{LL } (k = 3) = \overline{867 \text{ lb per ft}}$$
$$\text{LL } (k = 1) = {}^{300}\!\!/_{2}(3.75 + 0.58) = 650 \text{ lb per ft}$$

Selection of Trial Section

	Moment, kip-ft	Required section modulus, in.³
M_{Ds}	$0.060 \times 30^2 \times \tfrac{1}{8} = 6.75$	4.1
$M_{Dc} + M_{LL}\,(k = 3)$	$0.867 \times 30^2 \times \tfrac{1}{8} = 97.5$	58.5
$M_{LL}\,(k = 1)$	$0.650 \times 30^2 \times \tfrac{1}{8} = 73.1$	43.8

Assume 18 WF 50 with $A_s = 14.71$ in.², $d = 18.00$ in.,

$$I_s = 800.6 \text{ in.}^4, \quad S_s = 89.0 \text{ in.}^3$$

$$\frac{e_c}{d} = \frac{2.00}{18.00} = 0.111 \qquad \frac{S_s}{A_b} = \frac{89.0}{14.71} = 6.05$$

$$k = 3 \qquad\qquad\qquad\qquad k = 1$$

$$A_c = \frac{39 \times 4}{3 \times 10} = 5.20 \qquad\qquad A_c = \frac{39 \times 4}{1 \times 10} = 15.60$$

$$K_c = \frac{5.20}{5.20 + 14.71} = 0.261 \qquad K_c = \frac{15.60}{15.60 + 14.71} = 0.514$$

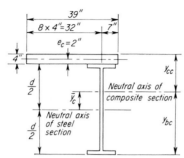

Fig. A-6. Design section for stringer $S1$.

From Fig. 5-1 for $k = 3$ and 1, respectively:

$$\frac{S_{bc}}{A_s d} = 0.398 \qquad \frac{S_{bc}}{A_s d} = 0.440$$

Bottom flange:

$$A_{Ds} = \frac{4.1}{6.05} \qquad\qquad = \quad 0.67 \text{ in.}^2$$

$$A_{Dc} + A_{LL} \ (k = 3) = \frac{58.5}{0.398 \times 18.00} = \quad 8.16$$

$$A_{LL} \ (k = 1) = \frac{43.8}{0.440 \times 18.00} = \quad 5.53$$

$$\overline{\qquad\qquad 14.36 \text{ in.}^2}$$

Try 18 WF 50.

Properties of Trial Section

Composite section with $k = 3$:

$K_c = 0.261$

$\bar{y}_c = (9.00 + 2.00)0.261 = 2.87$ in.

$I_c = 2.87 \times 11.00 \times 14.71 + 800.6 + \dfrac{5.20 \times 4^2}{12} = 1{,}271$ in.^{4}

$y_{bc} = 9.00 + 2.87 = 11.87$

$S_{bc} = 107$ in.^{3}

Composite section with $k = 1$:

$K_c = 0.514$

$\bar{y}_c = 11.00 \times 0.514 = 5.65$ in.

$I_c = 5.65 \times 11.00 \times 14.71 + 800.6 + \dfrac{15.60 \times 4^2}{12} = 1{,}736$ in.[4]

$y_{bc} = 9.00 + 5.65 = 14.65$ in.

$S_{bc} = 118$ in.[3]

$m = 15.60(9.00 - 5.65 + 2.00) = 83.3$ in.[3]

Stresses

$$\text{DLs} = \frac{6.75 \times 12}{89.0} = 0.91 \text{ ksi}$$

$$\text{DLc} + \text{LL } (k = 3) = \frac{97.5 \times 12}{107} = 10.91$$

$$\text{LL } (k = 1) = \frac{73.1 \times 12}{118} = 7.43$$

$$\overline{19.25 \text{ ksi}}$$

Shear Connector Spacing. Two $\tfrac{3}{4}$-in.-diameter studs per group:

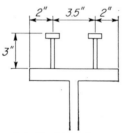

Fig. A-7. Stud location on $S1$.

$$2Q_{uc} = 19.5 \text{ kips}$$

$$C_{mc} = \frac{M_{Dc}}{M_{LL}} = \frac{24.4}{146.2} = 0.167$$

$$C_{mi} = \frac{M_{Ds}}{M_{LL}} = \frac{6.75}{146.2} = 0.046$$

$$C_s = \frac{S_{bc}}{S_{bs}} = \frac{118}{89.0} = 1.325$$

$$\text{FS} = \frac{2.4(1 + 0.167 + 0.046 \times 1.325) - 0.046}{1 + 0.167} = 2.49$$

$$p = \frac{I_c}{mV_c} \frac{2Q_{uc}}{\text{FS}} = \frac{1{,}736}{83.3} \times \frac{19.5}{2.49} \times \frac{1}{V_c} = \frac{163.3}{V_c}$$

It can be seen from $S2$ or the geometry of the shear curve that the connector spacing will vary inversely with the distance from the center line of the beam to the point being considered.

At the center line of bearing:

$$V_{LL} = 1.30 \times 30 \times \tfrac{1}{2} = 19.50 \text{ kips}$$
$$V_{Dc} = 0.217 \times 30 \times \tfrac{1}{2} = 3.25$$
$$V_c = 22.75 \text{ kips}$$
$$p = \frac{163.3}{22.75} = 7.18 \text{ in.}$$

At 5 ft from the center line of bearing:

$$p = 7.18 \times {}^{15}\!/_{10} = 10.78 \text{ in.}$$

At 10 ft from the center line of bearing:

$$p = 7.18 \times {}^{15}\!/_{5} = 21.56 \text{ in.}$$

Final Section

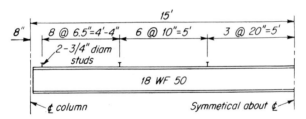

FIG. A-8. Stud spacing for $S1$.

G2—Assume girder weight = 180 lb per ft
Effective slab width = $16 \times 4 = 64$ in.

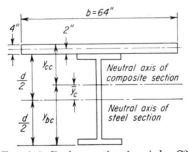

FIG. A-9. Design section for girder $G2$.

Design Data

	Moment, kip-ft	Required section modulus, in.³
M_{Ds}	$0.180 \times 30^2 \times \frac{1}{8} +$	
	$0.073 \times 30(7.5 + 1\frac{5}{2}) = 53.1$	31.9
M_{Dc}	$0.375 \times 30(7.5 + 1\frac{5}{2}) = 168.8$	
M_{LL} $(k = 3)$	$1.125 \times 30(7.5 + 1\frac{5}{2}) = 506$	
	$\overline{675}$	405
M_{LL} $(k = 1)$	$1.125 \times 30(7.5 + 1\frac{5}{2}) = 506$	304

Assume 36 WF 182 with $A_s = 53.54$ in.², $d = 36.32$ in. $I_s = 11,282$ in.⁴, $S_s = 621.2$ in.³.

$$\frac{e_c}{d} = \frac{2.00}{36.32} = 0.0551 \qquad \frac{S_s}{A_s} = \frac{621.2}{53.54} = 11.60$$

$$k = 3 \qquad\qquad\qquad k = 1$$

$$A_c = 8.53 \qquad\qquad A_c = 25.60$$

$$K_c = \frac{8.53}{8.53 + 53.54} = 0.137 \qquad K_c = \frac{25.60}{25.60 + 53.54} = 0.323$$

From Fig. 5-1:

$$\frac{S_{bc}}{A_s d} = 0.361 \qquad \frac{S_{bc}}{A_s d} = 0.392$$

Bottom flange:

$$A_{Ds} = \frac{31.9}{11.60} \qquad\qquad = 2.8 \text{ in.}^2$$

$$A_{Dc} + A_{LL} \ (k = 3) = \frac{405}{0.361 \times 36.32} = 30.9$$

$$A_{LL} \ (k = 1) = \frac{304}{0.392 \times 36.32} = 21.4$$

$$\overline{55.1 \text{ in.}^2}$$

Try 36 WF 194 with $A_s = 57.11$ in.², $d = 36.48$ in.,

$$I_s = 12,103 \text{ in.}^4, \ S_s = 663.6 \text{ in.}^3$$

Properties of Trial Section

Composite section with $k = 3$:

$$K_c = \frac{8.53}{8.53 + 57.11} = 0.130$$

$\bar{y}_c = (18.24 + 2.00)0.130 = 2.63$ in.

$I_c = 2.63 \times 20.24 \times 57.11 + 12,103 + \dfrac{8.53 \times 4^2}{12} = 15,140$ in.^{4}

$y_{bc} = 18.24 + 2.63 = 20.87$ in.

$S_{bc} = 725$ in.^{3}

Composite section with $k = 1$:

$$K_c = \frac{25.60}{25.60 + 57.11} = 0.310$$

$\bar{y}_c = 20.24 \times 0.310 = 6.28$ in.

$I_c = 6.28 \times 20.24 \times 57.11 + 12,103 + \dfrac{25.60 \times 4^2}{12}$

$\quad = 19,410$ in.^{4}

$y_{bc} = 18.24 + 6.28 = 24.52$

$S_{bc} = 792$ in.^{3}

$m = 25.60(18.24 - 6.28 + 2.00) = 358$ in.^{3}

Stresses

$$\text{DLs} = \frac{53.1 \times 12}{663.6} = 0.96 \text{ ksi}$$

$$\text{DLc} + \text{LL} \ (k = 3) = \frac{675 \times 12}{725} = 11.17$$

$$\text{LL} \ (k = 1) = \frac{506 \times 12}{792} = 7.67$$

$$\overline{ 19.80 \text{ ksi}}$$

Shear Connector Spacing. Four-$\frac{3}{4}$-in.-diameter studs per group.

$$4Q_{uc} = 4 \times 9.75 = 39.0 \text{ kips.}$$

$$C_{mc} = \frac{M_{Dc}}{M_{LL}} = \frac{168.8}{1,012} = 0.166$$

$$C_{mi} = \frac{M_{Ds}}{M_{LL}} = \frac{53.1}{1,012} = 0.053$$

$$C_s = \frac{S_{bc}}{S_{bs}} = \frac{792}{663.6} = 1.191$$

$$FS = \frac{2.4(1 + 0.166 + 0.053 \times 1.191) - 0.053}{1 + 0.166} = 2.48$$

$$p = \frac{I_c}{mV_c} \frac{4Q_{uc}}{FS} = \frac{19,410}{358} \times \frac{39.0}{2.48} \times \frac{1}{V_c} = \frac{853}{V_c}$$

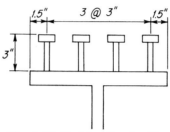

Fig. A-10. Stud location for $G2$.

At the center line of bearing:

$$V_{LL} = 67.50 \times 1.5 = 101.3 \text{ kips}$$
$$V_{Ds} = 11.25 \times 1.5 = \underline{\quad 16.9}$$
$$V_c = \overline{118.2} \text{ kips}$$

$$p = \frac{853}{118.2} = 7.21 \text{ in.}$$

At 7.5 ft from the center line of bearing:

$$p = 7.21 \times \frac{15}{7.5} = 14.42 \text{ in.}$$

Final Section

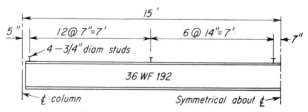

FIG. A-11. Stud spacing on $G2$.

$$\frac{e_c}{d} = \frac{2.00}{21.46} = 0.093 \qquad \frac{S_s}{A_s} = \frac{150.7}{21.46} = 7.02$$

$$k = 3 \qquad\qquad\qquad k = 1$$

$$A_c = \frac{64 \times 4}{3 \times 10} = 8.53 \qquad A_c = \frac{64 \times 4}{1 \times 10} = 25.60$$

$$K_c = \frac{8.53}{8.53 + 21.46} = 0.284 \qquad K_c = \frac{25.60}{25.60 + 21.46} = 0.543$$

From Fig. 5-1.

$$\frac{S_{bc}}{A_s d} = 0.397 \qquad\qquad \frac{S_{bc}}{A_s d} = 0.435$$

Bottom flange:

$$A_{Dc} + A_{LL} \ (k = 3) = \frac{106.2}{21.24 \times 0.397} = 12.60 \text{ in.}^2$$

$$A_{LL} \ (k = 1) = \frac{75.9}{21.24 \times 0.435} = \underline{8.22}$$

$$\overline{20.82 \text{ in.}^2}$$

Try 21 WF 73.

Properties of Trial Section.   (See computation for *S*2 and *S*3 in part A.)

Stresses

$$\text{DLc} + \text{LL} \ (k = 3) = \frac{177.0 \times 12}{181.2} = 11.72 \text{ ksi}$$

$$\text{LL} \ (k = 1) = \frac{126.7 \times 12}{199.6} = \underline{7.61}$$

$$\overline{19.33 \text{ ksi}}$$

Shear Connector Spacing.   Two ¾-in.-diameter studs per group.

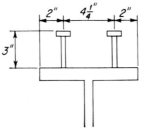

FIG. A-16. Stud location for *S*2 and *S*3.

$2Q_{uc} = 19.5$ kips

FS $= 2.4$ (see Eq. 27a)

$$p = \frac{I_c}{mV_c} \times \frac{2Q_{uc}}{\mathrm{FS}} = \frac{3{,}525}{148.5} \times \frac{19.5}{2.4} \times \frac{1}{V_c} = \frac{193}{V_c}$$

At the center line of bearing:

$$V_{LL} = 2.25 \times 30 \times \tfrac{1}{2} = 33.8 \text{ kips}$$
$$V_{Dc} = 0.448 \times 30 \times \tfrac{1}{2} = \underline{6.7}$$
$$40.5 \text{ kips}$$

$$p = \frac{193}{40.5} = 4.76 \text{ in.}$$

At 5 ft from the center line of bearing:

$$p = 4.76 \times {}^{15}\!/_{10} = 7.14 \text{ in.}$$

At 10 ft from the center line of bearing:

$$p = 4.76 \times {}^{15}\!/_{5} = 14.28 \text{ in.}$$

Final Section

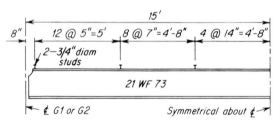

Fig. A-17. Stud spacing on $S2$ and $S3$.

The differences between the stresses and shear connector spacings computed in part A (partly shored construction) and in part B (fully shored construction) are negligible. This is usually true for building design, because the weight of the steel beam is small compared with the total loading. Therefore, it is sufficiently accurate to assume full shoring in most building designs.

ULTIMATE-MOMENT RESISTANCE OF
A COMPOSITE T BEAM

A composite beam carries the maximum load at the instant of crushing of the concrete slab. The corresponding moment capacity of the cross secton may be computed approximately on the basis of the following assumptions illustrated in Fig. A-18:

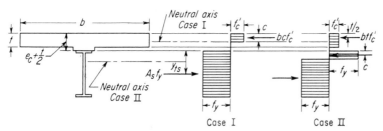

FIG. A-18. Idealized stress distribution at ultimate load.

1. Stresses in the concrete slab are distributed uniformly and are equal to the cylinder strength of concrete f'_c.

2. Concrete slab resists no tension.

3. Stresses in the steel beam are distributed uniformly and are equal to the yield point f_y.

The neutral axis may be located either in the slab or in the steel beam. If it is located in the slab (Case I in Fig. A-18), equilibrium of longitudinal forces gives the depth of the neutral axis as

$$c = \frac{A_s f_y}{b f'_c} \tag{A-4a}$$

The ultimate-moment capacity is then

$$M_{ult} = A_s f_y \left(y_{ts} + e_c + \frac{t}{2} - \frac{c}{2} \right) \tag{A-4b}$$

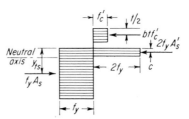

FIG. A-19. Equivalent stress distribution for Case II.

If the neutral axis is located in the steel beam, the assumed stress distribution is that shown in Fig. A-18 as Case II. This stress distribution may be replaced by the equivalent shown in Fig. A-19. The equilibrium of longitudinal forces may then be written as

$$A_s f_y - 2A'_s f_y = tbf'_c \qquad (A\text{-}5a)$$

and the area of steel in compression is

$$A'_s = \frac{A_s f_y - tbf'_c}{2f_y} \qquad (A\text{-}5b)$$

The distance c may then be determined from the compressive area A'_s and the dimensions of the steel beam. The ultimate-moment capacity is given by the equation

$$M_{uu} = tbf'_c(y_{ts} + e_c) + 2A'_s f_y(y_{ts} - c) \qquad (A\text{-}5c)$$

INDEX